SPEEDY

The story of an Irish pony from the days when she was a wild foal in Connemara. Speedy finds happiness in her first home where Terry breaks her in and thinks she shows promise for hunting and racing.

But she is sold and has to pull a van for her new owner. Yet Dan is convinced that she should be given a chance and in the point-to-point Speedy runs the race of her life.

SPEEDY

*

Esmé Hamilton

KNIGHT BOOKS

the paperback division of Brockhampton Press

ISBN 0 340 18004 8

This edition published 1974 by Knight, the paperback
division of Brockhampton Press, Leicester.
First published in 1940 by The Bodley Head
All rights reserved
Printed and bound in Great Britain
by Cox & Wyman Ltd, London, Reading
and Fakenham

Contents

*

I

Connemara

I was born in Connemara, where my mother grazed with a small herd of ponies on the side of a mountain. With us ran mares and foals, yearlings and older ponies, rough and long of tail and mane, and very footsure among the rocks and heather.

It was a treeless land of bog and mountain and lake, and we wandered for miles in search of the grazing that we shared with the little horny sheep and the small black Galway cattle. In the more fertile valleys the land was fenced with low walls half buried in purple loosestrife and rank grasses, and was patterned with squares of potatoes and oats, but we avoided the small farms and kept to the wild upland country and to the great sweeping moorland wastes that spread for miles towards the Atlantic Ocean.

My dam was grey, with clean, good legs and a keen little head. She was of Connemara blood and led the herd when we came down to drink in the evening, our soft muzzles making ripples in the clear bog water. As I raced about her in the sunlight, bucking on my long ungainly legs, she would turn her head to watch me, and call me with a low whicker through her nostrils if I strayed too far away.

The fuzzy-coated foals played together all day, jumping the bog drains and hummocks of heather, scrambling along the sheep paths on the steep slopes and picking their way warily over the bogs where a step off the track would have meant an ugly death for the pony that was careless enough to get 'bogged'. All day I played with them, while the rest of the herd slept or grazed, and in the hottest part of the day we lay in our mother's shade, listening to the cry of a curlew overhead, or the call of a grouse in the heather.

Sometimes, as we lay there, we saw an old woman in a red petticoat riding a donkey along the narrow road, or a boy that drove the black cattle along the shore of the lake, calling to them in a high thin voice. A river ran across the stones at the foot of the mountain, and across it in the valley a few white thatched cottages huddled among the potato patches. They were far below us like white pebbles at the bottom of a pool.

When I was a few months old I was standing with my mother at the foot of a slope, while the rest of the herd grazed or slept, when suddenly an old mare who stood sentry for us threw up her head and snorted.

Instantly the ponies wheeled round in alarm, and those who had been lying down in the sunlight scrambled to their feet. My mother stamped on the ground with her forefoot, and I huddled close to her side, and looked out under her neck to see what it was all about. Men were coming up the mountain towards us with dogs at their heels.

We broke up the mountain side in a bunch, manes and tails flying, only to stop with a slither as the leading mare sat down on her quarters and wheeled round again, for men were coming down the slope as well. I looked at them curiously as they came towards us. They spread out in a big circle so that they were on every side of us, and we were hemmed in on a little flat of rough grass and heather between the shoulders of the hills. The dogs ran, their tongues out, and laughed as we stood there, undecided and afraid. Then the stallion, a big chestnut with a sweeping mane and tail, made a dash to one side. They let him pass, but when we would have followed, the man on our side threw up his arms and whirled the rope that he held, and both his dogs ran forward, barking, so that we wheeled and plunged the other way.

Wherever we turned a man was waiting to head us back, and at last we stood, huddled, with the foals in the middle and the mares and older ponies on the outside. They began to divide us then, picking out a pony here and there and letting it go, and when they had picked us over, two men walked up to the mares that had white harness marks on their withers, and slipped ropes round their necks.

They did not seem to mind and followed the men, while the foals and young ponies, perplexed and nervous, moved forward, driven on from behind and watched for a chance to escape if they could.

When we reached the road we were driven along it for miles, white dust rising as we went and settling on our backs and manes, and as evening drew on we were too tired to think of escape, and only longed for water and a chance to rest our weary legs, unused to such travelling.

Late in the day we came in sight of more horses by the side of the road, carts were drawn up on the grass, odd-looking covered carts, painted red and green, with smoke coming out of funnels in their tops. Open carts stood with their shafts down, and to one of them a goat was tethered.

There in the hollow between the bank and the road women and children sat around a fire, they shouted to the men as we came, and their long, scraggy dogs growled at us from under the carts.

We were so tired that all we wanted then was to be allowed to rest, and when we were driven into the pond by the crossroads we drank and drank, the water dripping from our noses, and our tired hooves soothed by the coolness of it.

The horses by the caravans stood and looked at us, they were old and thin, with white harness marks on their backs and sides. Near them, some donkeys grazed or dozed with half-shut eyes, and a young piebald pony slept in the dust.

A little smoke blew across the road from the fire. One of the youngsters hobbled the mares and they began to graze, and we foals, and the young horses that were with us, forgot our weariness in hunger and grazed with them.

2

Caravan

EARLY in the morning we were on the road again. The heavy caravans were harnessed to three old horses, and two ramshackle carts followed them, pulled by a donkey and the piebald pony.

One or two of the women sat in the caravans, others walked with the men, and the ragged, barefooted children drove us along at the rear.

In front of me I could see the little yellow horses painted round the sides of the green caravan, and the canary that swung in its cage over the doorway, beside it a white goat was tethered on a wooden ledge and stood there between a tin bucket and a bundle of brooms.

We travelled slowly, from stopping place to stopping place, along the narrow roads. And day after day the caravans lurched along in front of us, halting to cook the mid-day meal by the roadside, and at night we grazed along the wide grass edgings of the lanes, or lay in the shelter of the hedges, listening to the murmur of voices from the camp, where sparks shot up through the blue smoke of the fire. In the circle of firelight the big red-headed man played on his fiddle a wild up and down tune that seemed to have no beginning and no end to it, and a red glow played on the faces, as wild as the tune, that listened. They were a silent people whose children had little laughter, and their dogs never barked. They went their way quietly and were gone in the morning, only the grey ashes of the cooking fire, discarded rags, and the wisps of hay in the shallow ditch, betrayed where they had been.

Sometimes we stopped for a few days at an open space

where gorse and brambles grew, and flocks of grey and white geese picked the short-bitten grass. While we rested and grazed the men and women went away in carts that were loaded with pots and pans and buckets, rolls of linoleum, and china ornaments to sell to the people in the lonely cottages along the mountain roads.

These women of the caravans wore shawls over their ragged skirts and blouses, and their long wispy hair was caught into an untidy bun. Some of them wore broken shoes, the others went barefoot like their children who paddled along behind them in multi-coloured rags.

Their faces were brown and lined, and the children's hair fell in shaggy fringes across their foreheads, unless it was cropped to the bone.

Their black or tawny eyes were different from the eyes of the people in the villages. The boys wore old coats and trousers, far too long for them, and cloth caps, so faded that no one could tell what their original colour had been, well pulled down to one side. They carried stout ashplants to protect them from dogs, and knotted coloured handker-chiefs round their throats.

Sometimes, as we grazed in the evening, a man would come and look us over, and then he would go to the cara-vans and talk with our men for a while. Presently they would walk over to us, and picking out one of the three- or four-year-olds, they would look at it and feel its legs, and then one of the men would jog it up and down.

After a lot of talking the stranger would put a rope round the pony's neck and lead it away, and we would not see it again, so that when some weeks had passed the herd was much smaller than when we had started. Several times our men brought in a new donkey or horse to join us.

At the end of the summer we came to a country of shady lanes and wide fields where cattle grazed, or stood in the shadow of great spreading trees. Here and there, there were woods, and square old houses with many windows, or white-washed farms surrounded by outbuildings. While we were passing through this country my leg began to hurt me where the long days of walking along rough by-roads had worn down the hoof. At first it was not bad, but afterwards it became a hot, stabbing pain that hurt me with every step I took. I limped more and more and dragged along in the rear, getting further behind as the pain grew worse, and my mother whickered to me to hurry as I hobbled slowly along behind her. At the stopping places, the red-headed man who was the boss of the caravan looked at my foot and tied a wet cloth round it in the evening. This soothed it, but it still hurt me to walk on and I hobbled painfully along the next day.

We were passing a high wall with a big gateway in it one grey morning, when a man came out on to the road holding a child by the hand.

He spoke to the red-headed man, who took off his cap and talked to him for sometime. 'That was a good pony you sold me,' the tall man said. 'I made a hunter out of him for my brother's boys.'

'You couldn't do with another, Captain, I suppose?' said the Tinker, and the tall man laughed. 'I've got too many young horses coming on.'

The child tugged at his hand. 'Look at the lame one,' he shouted.

I was hobbling along behind the grey mare, and the two men turned to look at me. The Tinker spoke, 'I'm taking them up to sell them in Dublin, but I don't think that one'll get far. She's a nice foal, but I'm afraid I'll be at the loss of her. Good-day to you, sir. I'm glad the grey did well for you.'

He moved off, and as we passed the gate the tall man called him back.

'I'll tell you what I'll do for you. You can throw the foal out to grass here for a week and fetch it on your way back, you won't get far with it as it is.'

The Tinker said he would be glad to do it, and one of the women put a piece of rope round my neck as I stood in the dust resting my leg.

'The blessings of God on your Honour,' she said, handing the rope to the tall man, while the child jumped with excitement and stared at the dark-eyed children of the caravans, who returned the look with interest.

The wheels began to turn, the caravans lurched down the road, and the horses and donkeys pattered along behind them in a ragged cavalcade.

I tugged at my rope and whinnied to my mother who stopped and whinnied back. All down the road I could hear her calling till they vanished in a cloud of dust. Then the tall man tried to lead me through the gate. I didn't like the rope round my neck and I had never been led before, so I stuck my toes in and pulled against it as hard as I could. He patted my neck, and putting his arm across my back, half carried, half dragged me through the gateway and off the avenue. The rope came off my neck, and I was standing in a long field full of clover and late buttercups and grazing cattle. I couldn't run away because of my foot, so I stood and looked, and the man and his child looked at me and talked to each other. Presently they turned and walked away, and I started to whinny for the grey mare, for I was very lonely.

Every day a boy with a bucket came and bathed my foot, and put soothing stuff on it, stuff that smelt good, and soon I could walk without pain and grew fat and skittish with rest and good grass.

The child used to come down to my field every day with a pocketful of oats, and I grew to look forward to his coming, and would gallop to the gate to meet him.

In the field there were several big chestnut trees, and in one corner of it was a shallow pond, overhung by white-thorns, where the cattle stood up to their knees in the muddy, olive-green water, and the sun made shadow patterns through the leaves.

In the evening, rabbits that had their burrows in the bank hopped out to graze along the headland, and wild duck flighted in, with a whistle of wings in the dark, to feed on the muddy edges of the pond.

I had forgotten about the caravan, when one day I heard wheels rolling down the road and smelt horses and dogs on the wind. I cantered across to the hedge and ran along beside them, whickering a greeting. There were the three caravans, and the long dogs that ran between the wheels, and the women and children in the carts. But the old mare was not there, nor were the donkeys or the foals and young horses, and I never saw them again. The leading wagon pulled up at the gate and the red-headed man jumped down and walked towards me. I kicked up my heels and ran to the other end of the field. I did not want to leave the long lazy days and go back to the road, so I would not let them catch me if I could keep away from them. I could see him walking up the long avenue that ran through the fields. He opened the gate at the end of it and walked up to the house. Presently he came back again, and this time John and the Captain were with him. John was holding his father's hand and asking very hard for something. They walked over to the corner where I was standing, ready to leap away if anyone tried to catch me. The Captain talked and the Tinker talked, and John stood and looked up at them. After a while the Captain put his hand in his pocket and handed something to the red-headed man. Presently he walked away. The caravans moved off with a rumble of wheels and a patter of hooves on the road, and John and the Captain stood and watched me as I bucked and galloped round and round the field.

I lived there while the chestnut leaves turned red and drifted down one by one in the frosty air; while the rain dripped through the bare winter branches of the beech trees; while three springs brought crumpled pale green leaves to the hedges again, and later drifted white hawthorn blossom across the pond.

I shed my fuzzy foal coat and short woolly tail and mane, and saw in the water the reflection of a bright chestnut yearling with white stockings and a star, as I bent down to drink.

The reflection quivering in the water changed and grew, till a four-year-old with long mane and tail saw itself between fat, white sailing clouds and waving hawthorn branches in the rippling mirror.

One evening Terry the groom came through the gate of my field with a feed of oats in a bucket. In his other hand he held a head collar, and as he led me down the lane towards the stables, I could not know that the years of my freedom were ended.

3
Terry

THE loose-box that I now lived in was light and airy, there was a window at the back and a ventilator shaft ran up through the roof.

The half-door opened on to the yard, and when I put my head over and looked out I could see rows of stables on four sides of a square, and an archway that led out on to the avenue. The doors of the stables were painted dark green, and the bolts and the hinges white.

Big white stones edged the square of mown grass round the pump and the old stone trough, and a pair of hound puppies rolled and tumbled there, and scampered away through the archway.

There was always something to see, other horses put their head over the doors, or Terry, and Jack the boy, went backwards and forwards to the stables. Horses went out for exercise and came in again. So that I was never bored.

There was clean wheat straw on the floor of my stable, a bucket of water in one corner, and a rack of hay at the back. I took several days to get used to the dry hay and oats that I was fed with instead of sweet spring grass, and I was frightened of being shut in, but I soon became accustomed to it. I had been handled and led about ever since I was a foal, so I was not frightened of Terry whom I had always known. He tidied up my long mane and tail, and in a few days I liked the feel of the brushes and the massaging of the wisp on my coat and muscles. I was cleaned all over and my hooves were shod.

Terry took me quietly through my first lessons. The

roller, the crupper that went under my tail, the breaking bridle, and the long reins. On a circle in the paddock by the hay shed my education started, there was nothing, to frighten me, Terry never shouted or puzzled me, and I learnt quickly and without fear. Sometimes I did not know what I was meant to do. Terry knew what he wanted me to do, but he had no way of telling me that I could understand, except by putting me into the easiest position to carry out the movement he wished me to make and encouraging me when I did right.

We went for long walks through the overgrown lanes, and Terry held the long reins while I walked in front, arching my neck and trying to chew the bit which I did not like.

One day, while one of the boys held my head, he put his hand on my withers and lay across my back with his legs hanging down on one side. I was uneasy at feeling the unusual weight, and humped my back muscles under it, ready to make a spring if anything hurt me, but Terry just stayed there and patted and talked to me, and smacked my back with his hand. Soon I got used to it, seeing that there was nothing to fear and he did this for a short time every day after we came from the paddock, and there came a day when he could swing his legs about and smack my back and quarters with his hand, and climb off and on until I didn't care what he did.

One morning, when he came to my stable as usual, Terry carried a big brown thing on his arm. Jack led me out into the yard and Terry held it out to me, I smelled it cautiously with my nose stretched out. It smelled oily, and I snorted and backed away. Terry put it down at my feet and let me get used to the look of it while he gave me a handful of oats out of his pocket. Then he picked the saddle up, while Jack held my head, and he brought it nearer and nearer till it vanished behind my withers, and I felt a cold hard thing come gently down on my back. I humped up under it and tightened all my muscles, ready to jump forward, but Jack held my head, and Terry stood and patted my neck till presently the cold feeling went out of the thing on my back and gradually I let my muscles go slack and looked about me. Terry spent all the morning taking the saddle off and putting it on again, dragging it gently across my back, till I no longer humped up under it when I felt its weight on me. Then he would smack the leather with his hand, and slap the flaps up and down.

The next lesson was a harder one, Terry took the girth in one hand and passed it underneath me and gently drew it tight. I humped my back when I felt it tighten, and Terry loosed it a little, slowly he tightened it up, and all the time I had a panicky feeling that something that I couldn't get away from was holding me. It took a good many lessons before I stopped humping my back when the girth was put on and pulled up.

He told Jack that half the battle was in the girthing. 'Girth them too tight,' he said, 'and look out for trouble!' Soon afterwards he got on my back, and Jack led me round and round, he did this for three days after which I took it as a matter of course, like my morning feed and the grooming that Jack gave me every day. I liked my grooming except when the brush tickled me under the tummy, and then I would fidget and try to nip Jack behind, till he smacked my nose and said, 'Give over, you.'

On the fourth day after Terry had backed me, Jack led me out and held my head while Terry got up. I had been out on the long reins that morning and was not too fresh. We walked round the lunging ring in the paddock till Terry said, 'Let her go now, Jack,' and I was walking by myself for the first time, with Terry on my back. I stopped, not knowing quite what he wanted me to do, and he pressed my sides with his legs, showing me that he wanted me to go on, I walked round and round the ring, and when he gave my mouth a gentle pull with the reins I stopped as I had learnt to do on the long reins.

Terry turned me to right and to left, using his opposite leg to the direction he wanted me to go in, so as to prevent my quarters swinging out as I turned. He wanted me to turn from my hocks, and not off my forelegs.

We did this for several days, riding through the fields and on the roads. We had never gone faster than a walk and we walked for miles.

In the long reins I had been taught to turn and back, to pull up and stand, and to carry myself correctly. To walk, trot, and canter, and not to mind the feel of harness flapping about me, the flipping of the outside rein against my hocks, and the pressure of it on my side.

One morning, when we came to the foot of a long hill, Terry pulled gently on the reins, at the same time pressing my sides with his legs. I bent my neck to the bit and brought my quarters under me, a quick pressure of his legs, and I started to trot up the long hill. It was a gentle slope and Terry gave me more rein when I was in my stride. I gave my mouth to the bit and got my hind legs under me, and Terry kept pushing me forward with his legs until I was trotting along collectedly, not sprawling about as I did at first.

Now I found that the weight of a man on my back was much easier to carry for it was distributed evenly over each leg, and this made my movements much easier and more free.

We trotted slowly up every long slope we came to till I learnt to trot steadily and collectedly, taking just enough hold of the bit to feel Terry's hand on my mouth.

Every movement he made meant something; when he shortened the right rein I turned to the right; in that position the easiest way for me to go was to the right. When he shortened the left rein I turned to the left, and which ever way I turned, the pressure of his outside leg kept my quarters from swinging out, and made me turn on my hocks instead of scrambling clumsily round on my forehand.

When he pressed my sides with his legs, and gave me the reins, I went forward, and when he closed his legs on my sides, and at the same time gave a strong equal pressure on the bit, I came to a standstill.

He never jabbed my mouth suddenly or made meaningless movements with hands and legs that would have bewildered me, he knew what he wanted me to do, and he knew exactly how to make me do it. So I learnt the language of leg and hand on rein, and I never forgot it.

I learnt to stride out at a walk, to carry my head well, and to trot both collectedly and with a loose rein. And in the stable Terry taught me the meaning of a double bridle, and to give my jaw the moment I felt the pressure of the curb. The moment Terry felt my jaw relax, his hand on the curb relaxed to meet it, so I knew that by relaxing my jaw, and so bending my head from the poll, I would at once ease the pressure of the curb on the tender bars of my mouth, and of the curb chain on my chin groove.

Nothing is more painful than the pressure of a double bridle if it is wrongly used, it holds your lower jaw, the most tender part of you, in a vice that can be agony unless it is relaxed. If you don't find release at once by relaxing your jaw, there is nothing to do but pull to try and get away from it. I learnt that later on.

Best of all our rides were the glorious mornings when Terry would take me out into the long field, and canter me in a big circle. First making me go to the right, and lead with my right leg, and then turning me round the other way and making me lead with my left. For when you are going in a circle you must lead with the inside foreleg otherwise you overbalance.

If you were galloping down a field and you turned suddenly and were on the outside leg, you might fall.

We never did the same thing for very long. When Terry wanted to teach me something, he used to take me into the field and there we practised it for a short time. Then we would walk and trot, or canter down the field, or go out into the road for exercise. We would do a little of that one thing every day until I was perfect at it, and then we would start to learn something else. Everything I learnt was for a purpose, to make me handy, to prepare me for the work I should have to do, and to make me a good ride. I loved those mornings, and would dance about when first came into the field, arching my neck for delight in the springy grass under my feet. Sometimes John came and sat on the gate, and watched me as I went round. He had grown quite big now and rode a fat white pony called Jumbo, who lived out in the long field. Jumbo, in the summer, was sleek and white, and his mane was combed. In winter he grew a long shaggy coat and looked more disreputable than Tatters the Sealyham, but whatever he looked like, John thought he was no end of a horse, and he certainly had great heart in him for his size.

4
The forge

'SHE wants a new set, Jack,' said Terry, picking up my feet one after the other. 'This lot are wearing a bit thin.' He looked at his watch and turned to go. 'You'd better take her yourself, Jack,' he said. 'I have to go to the station with the big horse. The Captain wants me to see him on to the train. Ride her quietly now, you'd better walk her, and don't let Rooney pare them down too much.'

Jack went over to the harness-room and came back with my saddle and bridle. He slipped the bit into my mouth and tightened up the girth. I stood quietly while he got up, but he felt strange on my back, and did not hold the reins in the same way that Terry held them. He held my head too tightly and kept nudging me in the ribs to make me walk faster, so I began to joggle and felt fussed and uneasy. By the time we got to the forge I was all on edge, and my neck was in a lather.

The forge stood in the middle of a row of whitewashed cottages, the red half doors were open, and through the narrow many paned windows I could see the red sparks of the fire fly upwards as the big bellows were pulled up and down. The wheels of a cart leaned against the wall outside and through the smoky dimness beyond the doors, loomed the quarters of a big bay horse that was being shod. Jack leaned against the wall and talked to Rooney the blacksmith, holding my reins over his arm.

There was a smell of singed hoof and hot iron and coal smoke, mixed with horse, and with the dust of centuries that grimed the walls and the old beams of the roof. Horseshoes and rusty iron of all sorts lay heaped in the corners of the forge, and on a sack a very old fox terrier lay asleep.

Rooney, in his old leather apron, with his shirt sleeves rolled up above the elbow, hammered a piece of hot iron on the anvil, hitting it into shape, the shape of a horseshoe, with shrewd blows, and then plunging it into the heap of coals till it came out white and glowing, when he would beat it again. His boy, Bill, pulled the great wood and leather bellows up and down, sending a shower of sparks up the wide grimy chimney.

The horse took a long time to shoe and presently Jack got tired of waiting. 'I'll tie her to the ring,' he said. 'She's as quiet as a lamb, keep an eye on her for me, Bill, I won't be gone a minute.' He led me into the forge and tied my reins to the ring in the wall. 'Untie her, Bill, if she fidgets,' he said, and went out whistling, while I stood quietly in the corner sniffing at the boards, and watched Rooney pick up the horse's forefoot and pare it with a curved knife.

He pared one hoof after the other, holding it on his knee, and cutting away the wall where it had grown too long. Then he took the red-hot shoe and fitted it to the hoof for a moment to get the shape right.

Whissssssssh! A cloud of smelly smoke shot up towards the roof, sizzling. Still on edge after the ride down, I threw up my head and sat back hard, the reins broke, and before I knew what I was doing I had spun round and bolted out through the open door.

The stirrups flapped against my sides, my head went down between my knees, and I bucked and bucked with arched back, fighting to get rid of the saddle in a panic of unreasoning terror. For the first time I hated it, and it would not come off. I squealed and reared up in the air, I bucked sideways and in a circle, still it stuck, and then I galloped up the road towards home, bucking as I went.

At the top of the hill some men who were breaking

stones ran out when they saw me coming, and threw up their arms to stop me. Slithering on the slippery road, I nearly fell as I pulled up suddenly. 'Woa, pet!' the first man said, and took my reins in his hand. He patted my steaming neck as I stood there, sobbing and blowing with excitement and fright.

Rooney and Jack came running up the road, they shouted excitedly to the men, and came up very much out of breath. 'I never thought she'd go off like that,' Jack said. 'You'd have sworn she was as quiet as a sheep.' They led me back to the forge and soon had my shoes off. Rooney pared my feet one by one, and fitted on the new shoes, hammering in the nails with swift sure strokes, and rasping the clinches with a file.

'She'll do now,' he said, wiping his forehead with the back of his hand, and Bill oiled my hooves with an oily brush and made them black and shiny. 'Put a hand on her while I get up, Bill,' said Jack, as he led me out of the door.

As he put his foot in the stirrup, and because I was still in a fuss, I humped my back under the saddle, and by bad luck, Jack dug his toe into my side just behind the girth as he swung himself up. I gave a bound into the air, broke away from young Rooney, and felt Jack sprawling on my back, half out of the saddle, with one foot in the stirrup. Down went my head, and I bucked with all four legs rigid as they hit the ground. At the second buck something gave, my back was lightened, and Jack flew through the air and fell with a bump in front of me.

Round and round the square I bucked, trying to get rid of my saddle. The broken reins that Rooney had tied together with string got tangled round my legs and brought me to a standstill. I threw up my head and snorted. Scared, and a bit shaken by his fall on the hard ground, Jack came towards me and caught my bridle. I backed away and humped my back, looking at him out of the corner of my eye. He put his foot in the stirrup and I went straight up in the air, almost upsetting him, but somehow he held on to the reins.

'Take my advice and lead her home,' said Rooney. 'You'll get no good out of her now, and you'll only get a bad toss. Once they learn they can plug you, when they're green like that, they'll try it again. Take her back and let Terry get the better of her. You might ruin her now if she plugs you again.'

Jack hated to give in, but he knew that he was no rough-rider. He pulled the knotted reins over my head and led me home. 'I never should have left her alone,' he said, 'Terry'll have the hide off me.'

'He'll tan more than the hide off you when he sees the state you have the mare in,' growled Rooney as he walked into the forge.

We went slowly home, I fidgeted, and bounded, and lathered, all the way back. When we walked through the archway Terry was waiting for us in the yard.

Jack told him what had happened. He was only a boy, and he had had a good shaking, so no one could blame him if he wiped his eyes on the back of his sleeve. Terry looked tactfully across the yard. 'I shouldn't have let you take her,' he said, 'I might have known you'd be off after cigarettes, she's in a nice mess, hop it now before I think better of it and take the two ears off you.'

He felt my legs all over and patted my neck, leading me into the stable. He lifted the flap of the saddle to undo the buckle, but at the first touch on the girth my panic returned and I went up on end, knocked him backwards. I bucked round the stable, my feet slipped at the corner, and I rolled head over heels on to the floor. That knocked the breath and all the fight out of me. I got up and stood shivering while Terry took the saddle off and slipped the bit out of my mouth. He patted and made much of me as he dried my lathered coat.

That night I would not touch my oats and hay, I was too upset to do more than gulp some water. 'Off her grub, Sir,' said Terry to the Captain when he and John came round in the evening. 'It's a thousand pities that it should have happened. I shouldn't have let Jack ride her; she felt he was strange.'

The next day I felt better and was hungry for my morning feed. Terry groomed me himself and spent the morning putting the saddle on and off my back and tightening up the girth gently as he used to do when he was breaking me. I didn't mind now that my panic was gone, and when he got up on my back in the yard, I just stood still as usual. There was nothing in the daily routine of being saddled, bridled and mounted to make me want to buck, and Terry never touched my ribs with his toe as he got into the saddle.

We trotted down the lane and went for a canter in the long field, I was happy and enjoyed the rush through the keen morning air. The next time that I went to the forge Terry took me himself and saw to it that there was nothing unusual to frighten me. When we came out I suddenly remembered, and humped my back, but Terry raised my head and sent me into a trot before I had time to buck, and I soon forgot all about it.

Sometimes for fun, and the feeling that it was good to be alive, I would throw a buck when I came out in the morning, or when we first got on to the grass, but I never wanted to buck again from panic or to get rid of man or saddle.

5
Schooling

JACK and Terry took me down the fields with them, they had fastened a long rope to the cavesson, and led me along until we came to a little ditch that ran across the field where the cows were pastured.

It wasn't very wide and Terry jumped across it on his feet; he said, 'Come along, Girl,' pulling gently on the rope. I didn't know quite what to do, I put my forefeet out to feel the edge of the ditch, and put down my nose, uncertain how to get over it. Jack was beside me, patting my quarters with his hand. Then I brought my hind hooves down just behind my forefeet and shivered on the edge. 'Come along then,' said Terry, and Jack brought his hand down with a gentle smack on my quarters. I couldn't go back because Terry held the rope, and I was afraid of falling in if I stayed where I was, so I put down my head to balance myself, pushed off with my hind legs, and landed on the other side. It was easy.

Terry patted my neck and gave me a handful of oats. 'Good Girl,' he said, and I walked between them to the corner of the field where there was a steep slide down into the stream at the bottom where the cattle drank.

Terry went down first, and Jack held me till he was standing on the other side. The stream was only a wet shred at the foot of the slope. Jack threw the rope to Terry, who said, 'let her go.' I didn't like the steep slope and pulled against the rope, but Jack took my bridle and led me up to it. I put a foot down, felt the uneven bank, and jumped back hastily. Jack smacked my quarters with the flat of his hand, and Terry pulled persuasively on the rope with gentle pulls. This time I put both forefeet down, and drew my hindfeet under me. I crouched on the edge, it seemed a long way down. For a few moments I stayed there quivering, then with a scramble and a rush I slid down on my hocks and walked out up the cattle path. We turned for home up the long field where the sheep were lying. There was a drain running across the middle of the field with a low bank on the far side of it, the sheep had bitten the take-off and landing free from grass and weeds, and as Terry started to run, holding the rope, I trotted beside him.

'Now Girl,' he said, and jumped across, and I skipped over with him, bounding on to the bank with a flourish of my heels as I landed. 'That's more like it,' he said as he gave me a fistful of oats, 'now we'll go home,' and we walked back to my stable.

Every day we went down the fields, and I followed Terry over little ditches and banks, wherever they were not overgrown with meadowsweet and tangled grasses.

We went up and down scrambly places, getting bramble leaves in my mane, and I learnt to feel the take-off with my forefeet on the edge of the ditch, to tell whether it was sound enough to take my weight, to bring my hind legs beneath me and spring foward off my hocks using my head and neck to balance myself with, and to throw my balance backwards or forwards as I took off or landed.

I learnt to land well out into the field when I jumped a ditch, and to slide carefully down a steep place, leaning back on my hocks with my forelegs braced for landing.

I was confident and enjoyed my walks across country with Terry, and when he came across the yard with a pipe in his mouth and a coil of rope over his arm, I whickered to him over my door.

Max, the Alsatian, came with us, and flew the ditches like a horse, with a swish of his brush as he landed. He would turn round, laughing, with his red tongue lolling out, and watch Terry and me as we came over.

In the autumn, Terry took me for long rides on the road every day, and I grew fit and muscular and hard. For two or three hours we would walk, and gently trot, through the lanes where the scarlet rowan berries were ripe and the leaves were beginning to show their glowing autumn colours. Then in the fields we went schooling where the growth was driven from the ditches by the early frost, for Terry was riding me over the ditches now.

I think Terry enjoyed schooling as much as I did, I had great confidence in him for I knew that he would never catch me in the mouth when I was in the air and upset my balance, or hurt my mouth as I landed. He would let the reins slip through his fingers just enough to give me perfect freedom to balance myself, and if I ever made a mistake he was ready to pull me together again.

Cobwebs, covered with dew, clouded the fields in the early mornings as we rode across them. Out of the rushes, in the corner by one of the hedges, a late brood of pheasants exploded, dissolved into twelve flying balls of brown feathers, and rocketed over the ditch. Hares, soft shapes with long ears, galloped swiftly into the mist. And when we had cantered once round a field the dimpled chain of my hoof marks in the dewed grass met us as we rounded it again.

6

Cub hunting

ONE morning in October Jack came into my box with a stable lantern, for it was pitch dark. He gave me a drink of water and a feed of oats, and though I thought it was rather early for breakfast, I was quite hungry, and I stuck my nose into the manger and soon cleaned it out. Lipping round the edges, to see if any of the grains had escaped, I could hear Jumbo munching and grunting next door. He was stamping on the floor with his forefoot, which was a habit that he had when he was eating, for he was a greedy little beast.

When I had finished, the door opened and Jack came back again with his stable lantern. He hung it up on a hook and it flooded the stable with yellow light, making my shadow dance like some enormous monster on the wall. I had crouched down and jumped away from that shadow the first time a stable lantern was brought near me, but now I hardly looked at it as it shot up to the roof.

He brushed me all over with the dandy brush, whistling to himself as he worked down from the back of my ears, along my back and sides, to my quarters, with quick, strong sweeping strokes. Then he got the body brush and curry comb, and brushed me thoroughly, cleaning the brush on the curry comb, which he tapped on the floor now and again, to knock the dirt out of it.

Terry used to insist on seeing a little grey heap of dirt on the floor when he came in and then he would run his hand over me, and if his fingers did not come away clean, Jack would have to start all over again.

'There,' Terry would say, ruffling back my coat with his forefinger to look at the skin. 'How can you keep a horse in good condition if her skin is all clogged up with dried sweat from yesterday's exercise. To say nothing of all the dirt it throws off. You've got to clean the skin, not just brush the scuff off the top of her coat, and don't let me catch you leaving dried mud in the creases under her fore-arms.'

When the body brush had done its work, and even Terry could have found no fault with my cleanliness, Jack would get a wisp of hay and wisp me all over till my muscles tingled and my coat shone. Then he would brush out my mane and tail and give me a final rub over with the stable rubber. He was picking out my feet, one by one, with a hoof pick, and I was nuzzling his shoulder, when Terry walked into the stable with my saddle and bridle. 'I'll fix her up,' he said. 'You put the saddle on Jumbo for Master Johnnie, he'll be out there hopping to be off in a minute, and it's time we started.'

He put a clean stable rubber on my back under the saddle, and tightened up the girth. I put my ears back and pretended to bite at him, and he pulled my ear and gave my nose a gentle smack. 'Quick, Terry, or we'll be late, it's nearly quarter past six,' said Johnnie in a fever of impatience, dancing up and down outside. 'Go on now, Master Johnnie, get up on your horse,' said Terry, then, 'Come here to me now till I fix that tie. I have an idea,' he said, peering at Johnnie in the lamplight, 'that somebody didn't wash his face this morning, or if he did, it was a lick and a promise it got.'

Terry led me out into the yard and swung himself into the saddle. Jack gave Johnnie a leg up on Jumbo, and we set off in the darkness that was just beginning to show the first greyness of the morning. We jogged along through the empty lanes, past sleeping cottages, and long misty fields.

Sometimes we pulled up to a walk and Johnnie talked away to Terry, their voices low in the half light.

As we went, the sky grew first grey then deep rose along the east, and presently the sun came up through the mist. Woods showed up in the distance, dark masses, that grew clearer as we drew up to them. They stood out green and brown and orange, beech and oak and dark Scotch fir trees.

We trotted along by the grey demesne wall, where a cock pheasant rocketed up with a great flurry and fuss of feathers, and Jumbo, his laziness forgotten, began to prick his ears and step out, his eyes keen and excited. 'He knows where he's going,' said Terry. 'There's the hound van.'

We turned the corner and there, in the wide gateway, was a scarlet van with high sides, between the bars of which tan and white hound faces peered, with brown eyes and moist black noses, yawning and whimpering, asking to be let out. Horses walked round and round on the gravel, their coats shining in the early sunlight. There were ten of them, their riders talking and laughing, or soothing a restive youngster that sidled and fidgeted.

Three men in long overcoats and hard black peaked caps walked up and down by the hound van. One of them had a keen lined face, scarlet from years of hard riding. He spoke to Terry who rode over and talked to him.

Two or three cars drove up and pulled into the side of the road; some ponies and a few young horses trotted up from a side lane, and then, with a clang of hooves on the hard road, and a clink of bit and stirrup, the Hunt horses arrived. They were big, good looking hunters, two chestnuts, a bay, and a big black horse with a white blaze.

The hunstmen and whips took off their overcoats. Their pink hunt coats glowed bright among the tweeds of the other riders as they swung into their saddles, and the pack came pouring out of the van and feathered round the huntsman's horse. He spoke to a hound or two that stood looking up at him, and then said a word to one of the whips, who moved off in front of the pack.

The huntsman's big black horse gave a plunge and a buck as he followed, with the pack all round him, and the second whip brought up the rear. They jogged through the gate and up the avenue, where the great trunks of beech trees rose up each side from a sea of laurel, and the field clattered along behind them, Terry keeping me away from the other horses as we trotted slowly at the back.

Beside us ran a man in an old cloth coat with riding breeches stuffed into his stockings below the knee. Straining at their lead, he held three tiny rough looking terriers with tattered ears and the look of having been through fifty fights for the fun of it.

The pack turned through a narrow gateway and trotted across a great field, and as I felt the grass beneath my hooves I wanted to give a good buck for sheer joy and excitement, but Terry kept my head up, and I danced behind the other horses, giving a little bound into the air when a young horse started to play up in front of me.

Our tracks criss-crossed and lengthened in the grey dew and the fresh chill air of the early morning tickled my nostrils, so that I snorted through my nose to clear it. Other horses snorted, and a youngster started bucking and squealing as we drew up beside the long dark line of the wood.

Beside the fence the hounds stood in a bunch, their sterns waving; whimpering, they looked at the covert and back to the huntsman, asking for the signal to go.

He held them there for a moment then waved them in, and they dashed forward, scrambling through the hedge in a mass of struggling brown and white, and scattered into undergrowth with a rustling and swaying of brambles and saplings, while startled blackbirds flew shrieking along the covert fence.

I did not know what it was all about, but I was very interested and excited, and could not stand still. 'Leu in, Leu in,' the huntsman called in a voice that carried across the wood. 'Yoi Try,' he called, and the long sound hung on the air among the trees. The two whips had galloped away and were somewhere out of sight. I could hear a whip crack at the far side of the covert, and the tapping of whipstock on saddle. Horses shifted about, tossing their heads and jingling their bits. Terry walked me slowly about, or stood watching and listening. The huntsman turned his horse and rode slowly down the line of the fence, calling now and again to encourage his hounds.

Sometimes, as the undergrowth crackled and rustled, a hound would appear on the bank for a moment, stand with stern waving and head up, listen for a second, and then plunge away through the brambles at full gallop. Little golden crested wrens, not much larger than a bumble bee, flew out of the covert and swayed among the white-thorn branches, and suddenly I heard a noise that I had never heard before.

It began in a whimper that rose and swelled to a volume of deep sound, and crashed and echoed through the wood in a fierce tumbling medley of notes. Every horse threw up his head, and stood with ears pricked, quivering with excitement. An old hunter who was next to me stood like a statue of himself, his eyes fixed on the wood, his fine old head alive with the expression of his interest as he listened to the deep clamour of the pack in covert.

They were coming towards us, and now I could hear the different hound voices in the chorus that rose and fell, deep notes and high notes tumbling over each other in their eagerness and excitement. Presently they dropped to a whimper and ceased. In the silence we could hear the huntsman speaking to his hounds, encouraging them. They worked about in the rough tangle of saplings and long grass near the covert fence, and presently they picked up the line again and hunted down the wood.

'Tally ho over!' I heard a whip call, and the huntsman came galloping out of a side path and turned down the line of the fence. The pack were getting further and further away and the horses that were with us turned and cantered down the field.

Terry kept me back until they were gone some way, and then we cantered quietly after them. I cocked my ears forward and wanted to stretch out my neck and race across the grass as I watched them galloping ahead of me with the sun shining on their hides. Galloping with other horses was the most exciting thing I had ever done, but Terry made me go quietly, and presently I steadied down. and my heart stopped thumping with excitement.

We drew up at a gate and stood in a bunch on the avenue where the huntsman was standing, watching the hounds working along the edge of the laurels. They spread out with their noses to the ground and their sterns waving. Then a hound picked up the line and whimpered. The others came galloping to her, and they streamed up the avenue into the far wood.

We stood on the avenue under the beech trees and switched our tails at the midges, and presently we heard the hounds hunting back towards us.

Watching the covert fence, I saw a red animal with white on its jaws and chest jump out over the ditch with a twist of his bushy brush and race across the field. The hounds came leaping out of the laurels, pouring over the ditch, and followed the line where the fox had been. They swept across the field, crying like seagulls, and the last hounds over the fence were galloping all out, to catch up with the body of the pack who were running fast.

The huntsman galloped along to the left and a little behind them, and as the two whips came galloping past us we followed. With horses on each side of me, their manes and tails flying as they went, I was happy and excited as I had never been before. The old horse galloped past us with his ears cocked. Striding along with great easy strides he watched the hounds, turning as they turned in the park. Presently the hounds ran into the wood again, and we pulled up and walked about, listening to their cry in covert and the voice of the huntsman cheering them on when they checked.

The sun was hot by this time, and the midges came in great clouds and settled on our hides when we stood in the shady places.

I tossed my head and stamped, swishing my tail about to shake them off when they bit me, and other horses walked up and down, or stood listening.

A whipper-in on a big brown horse watched the edge of the covert, tapping his saddle with his hunting whip or cracking it now and again with a whirl of the thong and a sharp report of the lash that made me jump when I heard it.

His coat was a scarlet splash against the wood, and as he turned his head from side to side watching to right and left to see that no fox broke his way, a pheasant whirred up through the brown and orange leaves of the beech trees and rocketed away across the park. A herd of cattle stood and watched us, fat little Galway blacks, that when the whip cracked curled their tails up over their backs and stampeded in a hurry.

'There's not an atom of scent now,' said the huntsman to the Master as he came past us. 'Sun's too hot.' Stealthily, a fox slipped out of the covert beyond the whip who turned his head to watch it and let it go. 'An old vixen,' I heard him say.

Suddenly, at the far side of the covert the cry of hounds sounded very loud and deep, and all in one place, marking. 'They have marked him,' said the whip, and galloped off to a gap.

The huntsman jumped off his horse and waded through the laurels, the whip's voice called by the earth a long cry, and the hounds echoed it fiercely. Then a man came running with three keen-eyed terriers on a lead. They had scarred muzzles and tattered ears, and they strained at the leash and whimpered as they ran. He carried a spade over his shoulder and a boy followed him with a crowbar. 'Come on now, Master Johnnie,' said Terry. 'We've had enough for the one day, they'll be all the morning digging out this cub, and the horses'll get destroyed with the midges.'

We turned back slowly through the fields to the gate and walked home through the lanes where the rowan berries glowed ripe among the turning leaves. I thought about hunting as I walked beside Jumbo along the brown road.

Something had happened to me that was more exciting than anything I had known in my life before. Horses had galloped past me and all round me, stirring in me the impulse to gallop with them, and then there had been the strange new excitement of the cry of hounds. That fierce wild sound that sent my blood racing and my heart pounding in my ribs when I heard it crashing through the covert.

Dimly I understood that when hounds ran there would be great pride in keeping my own place among the best of the horses. There would be intoxication in the long flight down the field with hounds running ahead and the wind whistling past my ears, in the feel of a big fence, faced, beaten, and flung behind. Somewhere at the back of my brain was the will to do well at this game.

Jack was in the yard when we got back, he gave me a warm drink and I drained the last drop in the bucket while he rubbed me down, and I ate my bran mash and thought how good it was. Terry and Johnnie came into look at me. I was not tired and had enjoyed myself thoroughly. 'That's the whole secret with a young horse, Master Johnnie,' Terry said. 'Always bring him back fresh and wanting more, and later on he'll never turn his head with you.'

'How did she go, Terry?' I heard the Captain say as Johnnie ran off to look at Jumbo. 'She was a bit excitable at first, but she soon settled down, she has the making of a real good pony, and she's not too hot,' said Terry.

'I took her along quietly, and just let her take it all in. They didn't do a whole lot this morning and we left them digging.' The Captain looked at me over the half-door for a minute. 'I have had bad news,' he said. 'I shall have to sell up.' I didn't hear what Terry said for they walked up the yard talking in low voices. I only knew that there was trouble in the air, and somehow felt that I was to have a share in it.

7

The auction

FOR several days there was bustle and stir in the yard. Carts were brought out of their sheds and washed and painted. Farm implements were cleaned and a man spent all one bright afternoon knocking and hammering at the big reaper and binder, taking bits out of it and putting them back again.

The next morning Terry and Jack were up early, carrying tables and chicken coops, furniture, farm stuff, and odds and ends, and putting them in rows round the walls. They cleaned and polished all the harness and stood the newly washed saddles out to dry in the sun. Jumbo and I, who were in boxes in the outer yard, looked out over our doors much mystified, and saw the three big cart-horses being led in. They were brushed and curried, and had their manes plaited with straw.

The young horses were brought up from the field and presently every box in the yard was full. The Captain came down when they were all in, and went from box to box looking them over. He seemed very down-hearted, and John was not with him.

For a long time he stood in the middle of the yard with his hands in his pockets and his shoulders drooping. He looked round at the stacked furniture, at the ploughs, carts, hay rakes, and harrows standing against the wall.

Then he turned and looked up at the square old house and the late roses that peeped over the brick wall of the big garden, and he walked slowly off towards the farmyards staring at his boots as he went.

Jack and Terry came into my stable in the afternoon and

gave me a thorough grooming. They put a bandage on my tail, and trimmed my fetlocks with scissors. 'Hard luck on the boss,' said Terry. 'He's like an old man to-day, it's broken him up altogether. My father worked for him before me, and you couldn't find a nicer man, and a great man to ride in his day. It's a pity he ever left the army.'

'If I had the money,' he went on, 'I'd buy Speedy, I never broke a pony I liked better, she has the makings of a real good hunter.'

'You get so fond of them you hate to part with them,' said Jack. They went out, taking the bucket with them, and I could hear them talking in Jumbo's stable.

I looked out over my door. The old house semed to be asleep in the yellow afternoon sunlight. A thin wisp of blue smoke rose from one chimney.

I could see the scarlet and yellow leaves of the chestnut tree in the long field drifting down, one by one, when a soft stir of wind loosened their hold on the half-naked branches.

Four years ago I had come here as an awkward leggy foal. I did not know where I should be to-morrow.

At daybreak the yard was astir. The horses were fed, watered, and groomed. My mane was plaited and the bandage taken off my tail. I looked out and saw Terry and Jack staggering along with a great crate full of squawking chickens. They put it down in a corner and went out through the gate. When the sun was high, streams of people arrived and wandered about looking at the stuff in the yard. Motors honked up the avenue and drew up with a scrunch of the gravel.

A man with a loud voice stood up on a farm cart, and shouted to the dingy crowd that gathered round him. At intervals he rapped on the board in front of him. This went on for a long time. 'The next thing on the list, gentlemen, are the store cattle,' he said, when all the stuff in the yard had been disposed of.

The herd drove ten frightened, milling beasts into the ring in front of him. They stood with their heads down and bellowed mournfully. The auctioneer talked; the crowd, their faces looking up at him, stood still. A man waved a piece of paper, another man nodded at intervals. The auctioneer knocked on the board, and the cattle were driven out again, to be followed by more cattle, and then by five roan dairy cows that had shared the long field with me since I was a yearling. They didn't like the crowd, and stood dazedly, with staring eyes.

Sheep were driven in, sold, and taken away again. Big drovers looked them over, nodding and talking to each other. Presently the crowd drifted away to lunch, and when they had gathered again, the auctioneer looked over his papers, put his spectacles on his nose, cleared his throat, and addressed them.

'Next on my list, gentlemen, we have the horses. The first on my list is a brown four-year-old by Redcourt. Guaranteed untried, and likely to make a high-class chaser. Sold sound subject to vet's opinion. What for the four-year-old by Redcourt. Bring him in, please.'

The four-year-old was led in, he threw up his head and stood there looking at the crowd which stared and murmured. The boy who held him trotted him up and down once, and the auctioneer cried, 'Will anybody start me at fifty pounds? Fifty pounds for the four-year-old by Redcourt.

'Twenty-five for him? Twenty-five I am bid. Thirty. Thirty-five. Forty, forty pounds on my right. Fifty, and the bid's against you in the gateway. Fifty for him. Trot him down, please.

'Fifty for the four-year-old by Redcourt. Fifty-five.

Sixty. Sixty pounds against you in the gateway. Sixty pounds and he's likely to make a good chaser.

'Are you all done? At sixty pounds and I'm selling him. Guaranteed untried, and out of the dam of winners.

'At sixty pounds ...' The hammer fell, the brown four-year-old jumped at the sound, and was led away, snorting at the crowd and tossing his mane as he went.

A grey filly took his place, and after keen bidding was sold to a dealer for a hundred and fifty pounds.

A two-year-old with a doubtful hock made thirty-five pounds and two brood mares and their foals went for a hundred and twenty pounds and ninety pounds.

Then the hunters came in. The Captain's brown mare was the first to come under the hammer, and she was bought by the Hunt for eighty pounds.

Billy, the short-tailed cob, bucked and plunged when he was trotted up and down. He was well known as a good performer, and was bought by a lady for sixty pounds. I heard Terry say to Jack that the Captain was doing much better than they had expected.

Presently Terry came up with a head-collar and led Jumbo out. I whickered to him as he went, and he turned his head and whinnied back. Terry led him into the ring, and he stood there proudly with his head up and his funny little fat body sleek and shining with good grooming.

'Jumbo. Well-known child's hunter, aged, sold subject to vet's opinion. This pony has been regularly hunted for the past eight seasons by children, and is sold without reserve,' read the auctioneer.

There was little bidding, and Jumbo was knocked down for fifteen pounds and led out of the ring. A small girl with a pigtail ran up to him and patted his neck.

'I'm glad you got him, Miss Mary,' I heard Terry say. 'Don't give him too much oats, and he'll do you grand.' He slipped the head-collar over my nose and passed the strap behind my ears. 'Come along, Speedy,' he said.

It was my turn now, and I stepped across the yard looking sideways at the strange things piled there. The dingy crowd gave way to let me through. I felt hemmed in by them; they were a great circle of shifting eyes in hairless faces, and their clothes smelt strong and rank. I pulled back and would not go into the ring.

Men waved sticks behind me and shouted. Terry said 'Leave her alone now,' and I went into the ring with a little rush and stood there snorting. The auctioneer sorted his papers and began to speak in his brisk voice. 'Chestnut mare,' he said. 'Fourteen three. Four years old, broken and schooled, and likely to make a boy's hunter. Sold sound subject to vet's opinion. What for the chestnut huntress? Trot her down, please.

'Thirty for her to start her? Twenty? Ten? Will anybody give me a bid of ten pounds for her? Broken and schooled, and likely to make a boy's hunter. No bid of ten pounds, and I'll pass her out.

'Ten pounds I am bid? Ten pounds on my right. Eleven, twelve, thirteen. Thirteen in the gateway. Fourteen on my left. Fifteen, sixteen, seventeen.

'Seventeen pounds for the chestnut pony; take her down again, please.'

I trotted down between the rows of faces, arching my neck.

'Are you all done?' said the auctioneer, as I came to a standstill in front of him. 'Going at seventeen pounds . . .

'Was that a bid, sir? Eighteen, nineteen, twenty. Twenty pounds against you in the gateway.

'Twenty-five, thirty, thirty-five, forty.' His voice went on, his head turning from side to side to watch the bids. I threw up my head and looked at him.

'Forty-five against you on my right, going at forty-five

pounds, going, going, are you all done? Going . . .' Crack! The hammer fell. I gave a jump at the sound and danced out of the ring, scattering the crowd and pulling Terry after me.

A man with a tweed coat and riding breeches came and looked at me.

He felt my legs and gave my shoulder a friendly pat. 'We'll take her down and get her vetted right away,' he said, and they led me down to the long field where a man was examining one of the horses that had been sold earlier in the afternoon.

He came over to where I was standing and felt me all over. Then he opened my mouth and looked at my teeth, ran his hand down my tendons, and picked my feet up one by one.

Terry trotted me up the field for some way and trotted me back again.

The vet took my bridle in his hand and turned me round in a short circle twice, looking at my feet as he did so.

Terry put the saddle on and cantered me round in a circle, first to the left and then to the right. Then we galloped round as fast as we could go, while the vet, standing in the centre of the circle, listened to hear if my wind was right.

When we pulled up and Terry jumped off, the vet took me into a nearby shed, and with a light he looked into my eyes carefully. He seemed to be doubtful about something, as he examined one eye closely again.

He turned to the man in riding breeches. 'I'm sorry,' he said. 'She's got a slight speck in her eye; it might never come against her, but I can't pass her sound. Her legs are good, her wind is all right, she is as sound as a bell otherwise, but I couldn't pass that eye.'

Terry led me away, and the man in riding breeches caught him up as we went back to the yard. 'I'm afraid she's no good to me unless I can make a bit on her,' he said. He walked away, and Terry slipped off my head-collar and shut the stable door. I was unsold after all.

In the yard the auction was still going on. The auction-eer walked into the house followed by the crowd, and people came out carrying bits of furniture, which they put in their cars and drove away.

When the auctioneer came back the Captain had a word with him; he nodded and got up on his cart.

'The chestnut mare is to be put up for sale again,' he said, and once more I was led into the ring.

This time there were fewer people, as most of the crowd had drifted away, and I was not uneasy.

'I am selling this pony without reserve,' said the auction-eer. 'You all saw her earlier in the day. She is sold sound, except for a slight speck in her right eye which is not considered likely to come against her.

'A bid of ten pounds to start her ... Is there no bid for the chestnut pony? Likely to make a good boy's hunter, and has good mouth and manners. Come on now! A bid of five for her?

'A bid of five on my right. Five pounds I am bid. Come on, gentlemen, I can't give this mare away.

'Six was it? On my left. Six I am bid. Seven against you. Eight. Nine, ten, eleven, twelve.' His eyes looked from side to side of the ring.

'Twelve against you on my left, thirteen, fourteen, fifteen pounds, and I'm selling her. Are you all done? ... All done at fifteen pounds? Fifteen pounds, and you lose her ...' Crack! The hammer fell, and a little fat man in a blue suit and a bowler hat took the rein from Terry as I came dancing out.

'You got her a bargain,' Terry said. 'Are you taking to hunting, Michael! Or is it a racehorse you are going to make of her! She's a fresh little mare, and she takes a bit of handling.'

'Well, she'll have to go the rounds the same as old Billy did,' said my new owner. 'Shocking bad hay weather this year,' he added. 'It wasn't fit to bed the cattle on between this and Cloneen.'

'God help the van!' I heard Terry mutter, as he turned to help Jack clear up the debris of the auction that littered the yard.

The next morning Terry came into my box. He stood in the doorway, and I walked over to him, giving a little whicker of welcome as I always did when he came to see me.

He put his hand under my chin and rubbed his face against my soft nose. 'Me poor old pet,' he said. I nuzzled his hair, and he gave my neck a gentle smack and walked away quickly. I stuck my nose out over the door and whinnied to him as he went, but he would not look back.

8

Connolly's yard

SHORTLY after my midday feed, a boy of about fourteen drove into the yard with an old pony and trap.

'I've come for the mare my father bought,' he said, and gave Jack the bridle that he held in his hand. He was small for his age, and light, with red tumbled hair, and grey eyes in a brown freckled face.

The pony he drove turned his head and looked at me curiously. He was very old, and his face and forehead were grizzled and flecked with white hairs. His under lip hung down and his back was hollow. 'Ah, poor Billy's day is done,' said the boy, as he and Jack looked at him. 'He'll have to go to the kennels as soon as we have the new pony broken to the van.'

He looked at Jack and his face broke into a grin. 'Do you think would I get a hunt out of her?' he said.

'Take my advice and don't put her in the van at all,' said Jack. 'She has the makings of the best hunter you'll ever get. Terry thought the world of her, and he's no bad judge. If she was my pony, I'd jump her in the show. You'd make money out of her, and as to being unsound, sure a speck in the eye'd be no more harm to her than a spot on your nose. What harm would it do her unless it grew worse, and I think it's nothing but an old knock she got when she was a foal. You got her a bargain if you ask me.'

Jack was showing off a bit, he talked like Terry, and he walked like Terry, he spat with great judgment into the gutter, and looked at Billy with a scathing eye.

'My father'd skin me if I asked him for more than an odd

day on her when the van wasn't going out. It wasn't much catch trying to hunt old Billy,' said the boy.

'He couldn't gallop to save his life, much less jump. I used to hate the sight of him when I saw them going away from me. But then it wasn't his fault the poor old skin.' He pulled the old pony's ear and came across to the stable where he stood and looked at me in silence for a while; he didn't know one end of a horse from the other, but he said the right thing.

'She's a nice one all right,' he said. 'Come on, mare,' and he led me out of the stable.

A younger boy, very like him, sat in the back of the trap, and he handed him the reins of my bridle, which were pulled over my head and run through one ring of my bit, behind my chin groove. 'Hold her now and don't let her go or I'll have your life,' he said to his brother as he climbed into the trap. 'Is she quiet?' the small boy asked Jack who winked at Mickey. 'You want to watch that one,' he said, 'she's a terrible passionate horse, she'd throw herself down as quick as look at you.'

'Goodbye now,' he said as he walked away, and the boy whose name was Mickey, gave the reins a flip, and started up the old pony.

As the trap rolled forward with a crunch of wheels on the gravel, I pulled back with a jump, but the reins had been run behind my chin and held as strongly. Jack turned, and waved his arms behind me, and I bounced forward so that my head was almost in the trap. For some minutes I fought the reins, pulling back, and being towed along with my neck stretched out and my tail tucked in between my quarters, while Jack ran behind me and gave me a hard smack with a little stick that he had pulled out of the hedge.

When I found that the trap did me no harm, and that hanging back meant a stinging smack on the quarters with

Jack's stick, it seemed to me that it would be more comfortable for me to follow quietly, and before we had got to the end of the lane I had settled down to Billy's shuffling jog.

Perhaps unconsciously I remembered travelling behind the carts and the caravan, at the beginning of my life, four years earlier.

We left the familiar roads along which I had exercised so often with Terry, and crossed the narrow bridge where the river slipped gleaming over the stones. And as we jogged through the village between the whitewashed cottages, and passed by the grey chapel and the new police barracks, we came to a country that I did not know.

We travelled for nearly three hours along brown roads free from tarmac, between ragged thorn hedges where loops of brambles, their last leaves wine-coloured, had leaped the ditch and embedded fresh roots in the green margin of the lanes, till we came to a high demesne wall, and jogged beside it as it twisted and turned, following the curves of the road.

The two boys talked to each other, the wheels crunched cheerfully as the old pony kept up the same steady shuffle for mile after mile, and the sun swung slowly across the heavens from east to south and then westward behind the tall trees.

Presently we turned a corner at the end of the wall and saw in front of us a tall white spire that soared into the frosty blue of the November sky.

Jackdaws like tiny black specks wheeled and circled round the top of it, high above the grey roofs that rose among the brown and orange leaves of the beech trees whose great branches were beginning to show, twisted and bare, where the autumn wind had stripped them.

Shops and houses stood on either side of a wide street, where here and there a horse and cart were standing by the footpath, and dogs and children played on the green square, under old lime trees that seemed to be hung with gold coins, so bright was the yellow of their leaves in the evening sunlight. We turned to the left, down a side street that ran between the low walls of back gardens where washing hung on lines; and presently the houses ceased abruptly and the fields sloped upwards from the river.

By the three-arched bridge stood a grey stone mill with a great wheel. Through the open door came the whirr of machinery, and men's voices shouted above the din. They were loading a lorry that stood close by with white sacks of flour, and the men's clothes and caps and their faces were white with flour and dust.

Mickey pulled up the old pony and jumped out over the shaft. He came round to the back of the trap and took my reins from the small boy who held them.

On the opposite side of the road rose a narrow, two-storied house of stone with a yard at the back of it, and at the side there was a small open shop where carcases of sheep and joints of meat hung on hooks.

Inside there was a long table and a rough wooden slab with a chopper on it.

The little man who had bought me at the auction put down the meat-saw that he was holding and came towards us, wiping his hands on his blue apron. He was a fat man with a bald head and a round red face. His narrow grey eyes inspected me carefully.

'How did she go, Mick?' he said.

'She was lepping about a bit at the start, but she gave us no trouble once we passed the bridge,' said Mickey.

'Jack says she has the makings of a great pony to ride,' he added wistfully.

'Jack says a lot,' my new owner grunted. His name was written up in white letters on the green board over his shop. 'Michael Connolly, Victualler,' it read.

He opened the gate into the yard and led me through it behind the old pony and the trap.

The yard was square and cobbled. On one side of it rose the back of the house with its green back door, before which a flock of chickens were fighting for some scraps that had been thrown out to them.

A low wall overlooked the river and the fields beyond, and on the opposite side was an open shed and a combined cow-byre and stable with red half-door.

Against the low wall that ran from the gate to the stable was piled a manure heap, and a great stack of elm branches for winter firing.

Mickey took the reins from his father and led me through the open door of the stable.

It was a rough loose-box. The back was of whitewashed stone, and the sides were boarded partitions with gaps between the upright boards that the light showed through.

The floor, cobbled like the yard, was covered with clean wheat straw, and a bucket of water stood in one corner.

There was hay in a wooden rack, and when Mickey slipped my bridle off my head I turned round, sniffing the floor and snorting. It was all strange to me.

I went over to the water bucket and sniffed at the water. It was good clean river stuff, and putting my lips thirstily into it I sucked down a long deep draught.

Mickey's father watched me over the half-door, while the small boy unharnessed Billy the pony and led him away.

'Did you ask what they called her?' he said, while Mickey knocked the dried mud off my legs and underneath with a handful of straw.

' "Speedy" I think the name was,' said Mickey. 'I heard tell the Captain bought her out of a string from Connemara.'

'Well, we'll leave it so,' said his father. 'It's unlucky to change a horse's name. Come on now and help me with the pigs.'

When I was alone I examined every bit of my stable, walking restlessly round it, smelling the straw and the walls.

I pawed the straw apart and smelt the floor. It smelt of strange horse, but the smell was faint and stale, and the stable must have been empty for sometime.

There were cobwebs in the corners, and a strong smell of cow came from the other side of the partition.

I put my nose to a crack in the boards and snorted. An answering snort came from the other side. There was a scramble and a rattle of chain as my neighbour jumped to her feet and sniffed and blew uneasily.

There were two cows there, and they chewed the cud solemnly. Sometimes they rattled their chains and their horns clicked against the bars of the manger.

I felt uneasy and upset; everything in this place was strange, and I was already homesick.

I wondered when Terry was coming to take me away, and I threw up my head and listened, but I could not hear either his voice or his footsteps. I put my head over the door and whinnied, but he did not come.

All the evening I walked restlessly round my box or stood with pricked ears listening. At intervals I whinnied again.

I wanted my own stable and the friendly yard with its familiar sights and sounds and smells. I wanted Jack to come in with his bucket and the hay-net and my evening feed of oats.

I sniffed at my hay. It was good hay, but I was too upset to touch it, and I ate nothing that night.

9
Dan

AT daylight I heard Mickey walk across the yard. A bucket clanked, and he threw open the top door of my stable, and unlatching the bottom half walked in.

When he saw the uneaten pile of hay he clicked his tongue, and taking my bucket he filled it and put it down inside the doorway. I drank greedily, and he filled the bucket up again and left it in the corner of the box so that I could have a drink when I was thirsty.

'Did you not eat your hay, Speedy?' he said, rubbing the back of my ear. He went out, and came back presently with a feed of oats. There was a little warm damp bran through it, and it smelt very good. 'That'll coax you now,' he said, as he held a handful under my nose.

I smelt it, lipped it a little, and then as I was really hungry I lipped it into my mouth and crunched the grain. Cautiously I lipped up the feed in the iron pot and began to eat, munching steadily and lifting up my foreleg in my eagerness.

When I had cleaned the pot out to the last grain and lipped about in the straw for any that was left, I turned to my uneaten hay and pulled a lock of it from the pile; I ate it, and then bent down for more.

Mickey went into the cow's stable, and I could hear the clink of buckets and the steady 'whit whit' as the twin streams of milk squirted into the pail.

When milking was over he carried the buckets away, and his small brother Jim unfastened the chains that were round the cows' necks.

They came out one after the other and walked slowly across the yard and through the gate of the paddock that ran down to the river beyond the house.

Presently Mickey came into my stable with a fork and started to clean it out, whistling to himself some tune that went with a swing and a jingle.

Like Jack, he separated the clean dry straw from the damp stuff with his two-pronged fork. The dry straw he piled in one corner. Then, bringing up the wheelbarrow that he had left outside, he piled the dirty bedding into it and wheeled it away, tipping it on to the manure heap that stood in the yard.

He came back with the yard brush and swept the floor of the stable clean, leaving it to dry for some minutes before shaking down some of the straw that was piled in one corner. The rest of the straw he left tossed up along the walls of the stable to dry until the evening, when it would be used for my bed.

Then he gave me a grooming, and though he was not so gentle as Terry or Jack, and was inclined to bring the brush down with a thump instead of a thorough brushing sweep, he cleaned me from nose to tail and did not forget to pick my feet out.

'Mickey,' shouted a voice from the yard, 'come on with that van. You should be gone hours ago.'

'Sure, I haven't got ten pairs of hands,' murmured Mickey in my ear. 'Coming,' he called.

'Did the mare grub all right this morning?' Michael Connolly wanted to know.

'She did when she got the bit of bran through her oats. She didn't eat a pick last night, but she seems less strange this morning,' I heard Mickey say.

Over the half-door I watched him fetch Billy the pony from the paddock beyond the wall. He left him standing in the yard while he fetched his harness, which he buckled on, and then backed him between the shafts of the van which he pulled out of the shed.

The van was painted green with red wheels, and Michael Connolly's name was written on the side on a square board.

It was a small open van with a plank across it for Mickey to sit on, and when all was ready the baskets of meat were brought out, the wheels crunched on the cobbles of the yard, and Billy shuffled off on his daily round.

Shep, the yellow sheep dog, ran between the wheels barking with excitement.

I stood in my box till the late afternoon, when there was a rattle on the cobbles and the van came back.

The cows were brought in and milked, and I was dozing with my head over the half-door, when the gate creaked on its hinges and an oldish man walked into the yard.

He might have been about sixty, he was light and fit, with alert grey eyes in a lined and wrinkled face and the neat look and carriage of a man who rides young horses for his livelihood. His slit of a mouth widened in a grin as he saw Mickey, and his face puckered into deeper creases.

An old cloth cap was on his head and he wore a brown polo-necked jersey, faded and worn like his brown cloth coat and the breeches and gaiters that he wore on legs that were crooked with years of riding.

Mickey went to meet him, and together they came over to my box.

For some time Dan looked me over in silence; then he spoke. 'Not a bad sort at all,' he said. 'She has a good length of rein to her and nice jumping quarters. I wouldn't mind being up on that one when the fox went away. Would he let you have a hunt on her, do you think, Mick?'

'I couldn't say whether he would or not,' said Mickey. 'I

never rode anything, only old Billy, and I'm afraid he'd think I wouldn't be man enough for this one.'

'Bring her up to the big field one day, and I'll show you how to ride her,' said Dan. 'Maybe I'll get up on her myself and give her a gallop round. I'm schooling a young horse now, and we might give them a jump together. How'd that be?'

'That'd be grand,' said Mickey. 'You won't say a word to anyone, will you, Dan, till he sees what a good one she is. And then he might let me have an odd hunt on her.

'Ah, bad luck to it, though!' he went on. 'He'll be saying I'd smash her up or lame her or something, and then he'd be left without a pony for the van.'

'Ah, well,' said Dan. 'Never's a long day! I'll be coming over one evening to put the van harness on her, and I'll take her down to the common to get the freshness off her before we try her with anything new.'

He walked away, and Mickey took my bucket to the pump and shut the stable door.

The shadows were growing long in the November afternoon when Dan walked into the yard again some days later.

Mickey brought out a saddle and a snaffle bridle and slipped the bit into my mouth, while Dan tightened up the girth.

They led me into the yard, where the chickens were fighting over their evening feed, and far away smoke rose up into the still air from a bonfire of potato-stalks that was burning in a tillage field across the river.

'Give me a leg up, Mick. I'm not as young as I was,' said Dan, and swung into the saddle. Once there I felt by the way he sat and the feel of his hand on the rein that he was more at home on a horse's back than he was on his own feet.

He ran his hand down my neck as Mickey opened the

gate on to the road, and we jogged along the footpath till we came to a lane that led off the tarred main road.

We crossed a bridge over the canal and trotted between the hedges till we came to the common called the Back of Beyond, where gorse bushes grew in clumps and cattle grazed.

Here and there were shallow gravel pits, disused and overgrown with grass. Shallow drains with low cattle-trodden banks crossed the common from one side to the other, and from end to end of it ran a narrow road with a small watery ditch on each side. A low white cottage stood by the roadside where the common ended and the fields began.

The late light had dyed the rushes golden-brown, and the distant line of the mountains stood out clearly above the landscape that carried the purple bloom of autumn-tinted trees and hedges.

Dan slowed down to a walk, and as we came on to the grass he turned me round and put me at the open ditch on the left side of the road. I cocked my ears and popped over it.

I loved jumping, and as we cantered gently across the short-cropped grass one of the long low gorse-bushes lay across our path, and Dan put me at it.

It reminded me of the gorse-stuffed hurdles in the long field at home that Terry used to jump me over. We cantered up to it, and I flew the green furze, taking it in my stride, and cantered on.

The grass ended in rushes and moss, and pulling up to a walk we splashed through them, putting up some snipe that rose with a harsh cry and zigzagged away with a flash of white underside and a flicker of wings, getting higher and higher until they were lost to view.

I was enjoying myself. It was a lovely evening with a touch of frost in the air, and every tree and bush in the countryside stood out sharply in the soft yellow light of the evening sun.

A young horse standing on one of the grassy hummocks was silhouetted against the frosty sky. He watched me cantering across the grass, and snorted.

I jumped on to a bank between two low bushes and saw below me a shallow ditch full of water.

Dan gave me a nudge with his legs, and I pushed off from my hocks and landed out over it. 'Now what about it?' said Dan. He turned me round, and I gave a bound of excitement, cocked my ears and sprang up over the ditch and well on to the top of the bank.

'You can jump all right,' I heard him mutter, and he trotted me slowly down by the blackthorn fence, bright with berries and wild rose hips and the leaves of looping brambles.

We walked slowly towards home as the frost smoke gathered on the horizon, blurring its pale primrose, and as we turned in at the gate Mickey was waiting for us.

'She can jump all right,' said Dan. 'I remember seeing her out cubbing one morning about a month ago, with Terry Flanagan on her. I was riding a young horse at the time. She seems to have a bit of speed about her too.' He took off my saddle and bridle, and Mickey gave my back a rub with a wisp of straw and bedded me down for the night.

10

Strange harness

'MICKEY,' said Dan, as we came in from a short ride the next afternoon. 'Will you get me the van harness.' He took off my saddle and bridle, slipped the head-collar over my head and led me out into the yard.

'Always take the freshness off them before you try them with anything new, and you won't have half the trouble,' he told Mickey, as he buckled the big collar round my neck.

I wanted to kick when I felt the crupper under my tail; but I had had it on before when I was being broken, and Dan kept me standing there until my back came down and then led me about the yard until I was used to the feel of it.

The next day, and for several days afterwards, Dan came in the morning, soon after the cows had been milked, and took me for a ride. Then he put on the van harness and drove me about in long reins, turning me to left and right and making me go forward to the command 'Go on,' pull up at the word 'Woa,' and back when he said 'Hike.'

As soon as I understood what he wanted and was indifferent to the feel of strange harness, the traces were fastened to a log and chain and I was made to pull it round the field.

'We'll try her in the old trap to-morrow,' said Dan. And the next morning they pulled the old trap out of the shed and picked a clucking hen off one of the moth-eaten cushions.

'Put the head-collar on under the bridle, and we'll lead her off that,' Dan told Mickey, and they buckled on my harness and fastened the traces. 'Just walk the other side of her, and we'll lead her down the road a bit.'

I walked forward, listening to the unfamiliar scrunch of the wheels behind me, stepping along between Mickey and Dan with my tail tucked in.

Presently I forgot the newness of the sound at my heels and looked down the road at some sheep that were coming along it in a big drove and bleating noisily.

'Hold her now, Mickey, while I get in,' said Dan, when they had passed. Mickey held my head, I felt the shafts tilt up for a moment and go forward again, and then the feel of Dan's hand on the reins. He was sitting in the trap, and as Mickey led me forward we walked down the road.

'Do you see the way I have the reins?' said Dan. 'Never let her slop along, or if she does anything, shies or slips or plays up, you won't have any control over her. You want to drive her much the same as if you were riding her. I hate to see a feller driving a horse along any old how; and another thing, this is a very different bit of stuff from old Billy, and she'll rattle along at any pace you drive her at. But take my advice and don't knock the legs off her, or she'll be no good for riding or anything else.

'Now that's a good pony, and I have an idea we'll make something out of her before we're done. You bring her up to my place sometime, and I'll show you how to ride her properly. We'll see if we can't get round the father to let you hunt her. I'm not saying anything, and it's too early now to go calling her a racehorse, but if she was mine I'd be trying to pick up a cobs' race with her before she was much older.'

'Do you think so, Dan?' Mickey's voice was filled with excitement. 'I don't know would the father ever let us, and who would we get to ride her?'

'Time enough for that when we have her in for a race. Don't say a word now until I have your father fixed, and mind now!' Dan paused and tapped the butt of the whip on Mickey's shoulder. 'There's to be no battering along the road, standing up in the van like those milk-van lads of Mooney's.

'I was riding along by Clonaney the other day, and here comes me young feller, haring along the road as if the hounds were after him, and the pony in a muck sweat, to say nothing of the racking the van was getting over the potholes.

'Hammer her along those roads, and there'll be no hunting for you and no cobs' race either, for legs won't stand it. Mind you, I know what it is myself when you have something you can fly along with.

'Now lead her on, and we'll go down the road for a bit.'

Two days later Dan got into the trap and took the driving reins in his hands. Mickey walked beside me for some way, but without touching my head, and Dan drove me along at a walk.

'You may leave her now, Mick,' he said. And Mickey went back to the yard to feed the pigs that were squealing for their buckets of scraps and swill.

For some way we walked down the road, and presently Dan put me into a trot and we bowled along the untarred side road, past cottages where the washing hung on lines and cackling hens ran across the road in front of us.

As we turned a corner we met the harriers coming home. We passed them at a crossroads, and Dan pulled me up by the side of the lane.

He got down and held my head, giving my neck a pat.

The huntsman and whip wore dark-green coats. They rode quietly one behind the other, talking of the day's work.

One of the hounds smelt something in the opposite ditch and trotted across to investigate. A sharp word, 'Verity,' and she slipped back to her place with her stern down and a guilty look in her eye.

The whip rode in front of the pack, his big chestnut horse striding along with ears pricked and mane ruffled by the wind.

There was mud on its quarters, and mud too on the whip's shoulder and on the dark-blue cap that he wore.

The huntsman rode a brown mare with a lean head and tan muzzle; two or three hounds trotted close to him, looking up and waving their sterns. He spoke their names and talked to them.

The rest of the pack jogged along behind the whip's horse, with wise wistful faces and flapping brown ears.

They were smaller than the foxhounds, I thought.

As they came towards us the whip held out his hunting-crop at arm's length. The long thong hung down, and the pack crowded together to one side of the road. He grinned at Dan as they jogged past, and the huntsman spoke a few words to him, something about coming to see a young horse.

They passed with a clatter of iron on stone, a gleam of bit and stirrup, and a patter like the dry rustle of leaves from the leathery pads of fifteen couple of hounds. I fidgeted and danced and longed to follow them.

The brown mare looked at me as she went by and whickered through her nostrils. I knew her at once. She was the same mare that the Captain had hunted, and she had been sold at the auction.

She looked well and in very good condition.

Two young horses jogged slowly towards us, and their riders stopped to talk to Dan.

I watched the hounds going away till the green coats looked black in the distance and the sound of the hooves was lost. I saw them cross the bridge over the canal, silhouetted against the afternoon sky.

Above them towered the white spire, soaring upwards, and wisps of blue smoke rose from the colour-washed houses beyond the bridge.

Then they turned off along the canal bank and I saw them no more. In their place came the memory of that early morning in October. I saw horses galloping, manes and tails flying, their riders standing up in their stirrups, leaning slightly forward.

I heard the full-throated crying of the pack as it raced down the long field.

I saw horses standing by the oak wood or walking about in the wet grass.

Once more I heard the horn and felt Terry's hand on the rein.

I woke with a start from my dreaming. Dan was saying 'Come on now.' He took up the reins. The two young horses trotted off, tossing their manes. They were big well-bred horses, over sixteen hands and beautifully made. A dark brown and a bay.

A car swung past us, slowing down at the corner, then another and another followed by some led horses jogging slowly with mud on their legs and flanks.

I trotted quietly past them all, curious and interested, but no longer startled. I had given up shying at stone heaps and logs and tar barrels at the side of the road.

When we crossed the bridge we met a steam-roller at work. There were five or six men in their shirt sleeves strewing stone chippings on the road.

They had sprayed hot tar across the surface and were covering it with broken stone. A water-cart with an old white horse was standing to one side. Near-by stood a big boiler on wheels filled with hot molten tar; steam rose from it and a pungent tarry smell.

The steam-roller moved forward across the newly laid

down chippings with a clanking, grinding, crunching noise
and a hiss of steam.

The man who drove it, his face black with oil and grime,
showed white teeth in a gleaming grin as he saw Dan
coming.

He stopped the steam-roller and leaned out to see what I
would do.

This time I was really frightened. I trotted up cautiously
with ears pricked: then the unusual shapes and the hiss of
steam and smell of tar were too much for me. I stopped
dead with forefeet out and tried to whip round.

One of the men came to my head and led me forward.
Very slowly I forced myself to go past the hissing, evil-
smelling, black shape.

I stepped gingerly, edging away from it, one eye watching for it to come towards me, but it did not move.

When I was past it, Dan turned me round and made me
stand there while it clanked and ground backwards and
forwards along the road.

I decided that it was nothing to be afraid of after all,
merely an evil-looking blood brother of the tractors and
haulage lorries that clanked and roared along the roads
and down the street, and which were evidently harmless
except for the noise and the smell and the dust that they
raised.

I had come to accept them as part of my surroundings,
and as I watched the roller for a while I lost all fear of it
and soon lost interest in it as Dan talked to the men. Then
we turned and trotted slowly home.

Soon afterwards Mickey came in the trap with us. He
took the reins from Dan and drove me along the bog road
between the bare hedges and across the commons where
the rushes and gorse bushes grew.

It was a fine bright afternoon and as we travelled, sometimes trotting, sometimes walking, crows swept across the

road from stubble to grassland and back again, wheeling and talking, while starlings whirred up in a brown mass, spread into a cloud, wheeled into a great globe of chattering bodies, fanned out, gleaming, and lit on another corner of the field.

Robins sang small broken trills of song from the hedges, and grey flocks of pigeons, hundreds strong, flew in the yellow light from beechwood to beechwood.

There was a smell of burning weeds in the air. The wheels ground lightly over the untarred brown-grey surface of the lane, and my own swift hooves beat out the rhythm of our going as I trotted along, ears cocked, at peace with the world.

II

The work of the day

ALTHOUGH I went with the van to many houses and farms, bringing them their weekly orders of meat, I did not always do the road work.

Michael Connolly had some land up the lane and sometimes I was needed there.

There was a big field, where thin store cattle found a sparse living in winter on the short-bitten grass. One of my jobs was to bring them fodder from the yard, oat straw, and hay in the small cart, whose wooden iron-shod wheels rattled as they went.

When we drove into the field, the cart bumping and swaying in the ruts at the gate, the cattle would come galloping and bellowing and follow the cart hungrily till it came to a standstill.

Then Mickey stood on top of the load, throwing down fodder with a pitchfork.

The next field was in tillage. Here Michael Connolly grew oats, the mangols that fed his cow and twenty ewes, and the potatoes and cabbage that with other things helped to feed himself and his family.

The third and smaller field had been a meadow that summer, and the sheep who had eaten down the aftergrass lived there and eked out the pasture with the mangols that I carted to them.

This was heavier work than trotting along with the van; but I was fit, and when the land was dry enough and the wheels did not stick in the mud and ruts I did not mind it, provided that my harness fitted me properly and did not rub or pinch me anywhere.

Once the stitches of my girth worked loose, and a hard piece of leather rubbed a long narrow strip of skin and hair off my side.

Again and again I dropped into a walk, breathing heavily at each step with the pain of it, but Mickey did not discover what was wrong until he brought me home.

In a week, after many dressings, the wound skinned over and the hair began to grow, but ever since I have carried a long white stripe down my side, for the hair grew white where the sore had been.

Sometimes I was harnessed into the tub trap, and Connolly would drive me to some farmhouse, often miles away, where I would stand with a rug thrown over me. My nosebag with some oats in it was put on and he would walk off down the fields with the farmer who owned the place.

Often he bought a fat heifer or young bullock, or a sheep or two that would presently hang head downwards or carved into neat joints from the hooks in the shop on Fridays.

Sometimes high crated sides were put on to the cart, and Mickey drove me to some yard behind a long colour-washed farmhouse, where fat young pigs were brought out squealing and put into the cart. I hated pigs; they smelt and squealed all the way back, and though I got used to them I fidgeted and pulled when we started down the muddy lane towards home.

Days with the March wind blowing through the bare branches followed a soft damp February, and now there was exhilaration in the air and dappled patches of sunlight and branch shadows on the trunks of the beeches.

The wind swept the country, never so bare and tidy as it was at this season, with all grass bitten short to the ground, no leaves, no growth, and all last year's dead leaves swept into the bottoms of the hedges or rotted away into the rich soil.

'You can take that mare out and give her some exercise when there's nothing for her to do,' said Connolly, as he came into the yard with the tub trap. I had given him an exciting drive that day, for it had been an idle week and I was on my toes in the keen air. I don't think he had enjoyed it much. 'Ride her, do you mean?' asked Mickey. 'Take the sass out of her any way you like,' said his father. 'She was like a mad thing this morning coming down the road.'

There was a joyful grin on Mickey's face as he unharnessed me in the yard. I wondered why he had given me twice my normal feed of oats the night before.

With regular work and enough oats to keep me fit but not more, I never wanted to bounce or fidget when Mickey rode me into the big field or through the lanes. I was fond of him, and would whicker a welcome over the half-door when I saw his red head and small snub-nosed face coming across the yard.

Cautiously at first, then with increasing confidence, he rode me when there was no other work for me to do.

One afternoon as we came to the common Mickey put me at the small ditch off the road.

I had not jumped a ditch since Dan had ridden me, and I cocked me ears and bounded over, giving a buck of excitement when I landed.

There was a flying shadow on the grass, and Mickey hit the ground with a thud under my nose.

He held on to the reins and scrambled into the saddle again.

With determination in every line of his small body, he put me at the open drain that ran across the common. This time I did not buck, and though Mickey fell on my neck as

I landed he pushed himself back into the saddle and recovered his lost stirrups without coming off.

We jumped the ditch again, and this time he gripped me tightly with his knees and let me have the reins as I reached forward so that I did not pull him over my head as I jumped.

That was better, and by the end of the month he was sitting more firmly in the saddle, though he fell off once or twice when I jumped sharply or gave a wider jump than usual.

We jumped the small bank in the corner, and as I landed the bit gave me a bang on the bars of my mouth that was sharp pain and hurt for as long as the bruise remained. Mickey had been left behind, and his body swinging back had jerked the reins and hurt my sensitive mouth. We turned to jump the fence again and afraid that the same thing would happen, I stuck in my toes and refused it.

'Go on now, go on,' said Mickey, kicking me in the ribs. There was one way to stop this annoyance, and I put down my head and kicked. Mickey came off.

Sitting with the reins in his hand, he looked at the fence and looked at me. Then he got up again and rode me over to the little drain. As we came up to it he gripped me tightly with his knees and catching hold of my mane threw me the reins as I jumped. There was no interference with my mouth and we rode home quietly, but any pressure of the bit hurt my sore bars for days afterwards.

I had always liked jumping, and now that Mickey no longer jerked my mouth or swung back in the saddle and bumped my loins we cantered at the small fences on the common and flew over them.

Mickey fell off and got on again, but always managed to hang on to the reins, and I never got away from him, though I found it hard to avoid stepping on him once or twice. He took some hard falls on the common before he learnt to sit on, but he always had another try.

'Ah, bad luck to it,' he would say, wiping the mud off his hands, and he'd hop round with one toe in the stirrup till he got a purchase on the saddle and swung himself up. Then he would take me back for a few paces and go at the fence again.

Dan had told him, whatever he did, not to hang on to the reins when he jumped.

It was a proud day for Mickey when he could canter me round all the drains on the common without coming off. They were wide drains, most of them, and one of them had a bank on the side next to the road. Then we would look for every gorse bush that we could find and practise over that.

I enjoyed those mornings later in the spring, when snipe were drumming over the brown rushes and the gorse was yellow with bloom. Then blackthorn came out in the hedges as if snow still drifted, and everywhere trees were breaking into crumpled leaf, for it was an early season and in April the young grass was heavy in the fields. Sometimes we startled a hare, and Mickey would whoop, and we would chase it across the common to the bounds fence and watch it scud across the field till it was out of sight.

One day at the end of March we were riding in the big field, when Mickey trotted me up to the wide ditch that separated it from the tillage field.

There was a high bank on the landing side, and the ditch was deep and matted here and there with ferns and brambles. Instead of taking it fairly fast he tried to make me jump it from a stand. I suppose he thought he would feel safer in the saddle if we took it slowly.

I looked at it, put my head down and sprang across. I landed half-way up the bank on the other side. Mickey had not been leaning forward as I took off and he got left behind the saddle.

I struggled to get up the bank, but my head was pulled up by his weight on the reins, so that I could not balance myself and could only paw the air. My hind legs slid, and I came over sideways into the ditch. I lay in the mud for a minute; then as the ditch was wide enough I got up and stood, fetlock deep in wet mud and water.

Then I got in a panic. I had never felt closed in like this before. I plunged along the ditch, bursting my way through the briars. I could not find a way out and the more I felt shut in the more I was frightened. The inherited fear of being bogged rose up in me, and I struggled blindly to get away.

Mickey had slid off over my tail as I fell and scrambled up the bank. He caught my reins as I plunged about and led me down the ditch to a cattle pass at the end of it.

Such a thing had never happened to me before, and I was very upset; but I had not hurt myself, and Mickey got into the saddle again.

Taking me back a few lengths into the field, he trotted me at the fence. I was frightened that I might fall now, and I whipped round just as we came to it, but Mickey held me at it and urged me on with his legs.

I put my head down, hesitated for a second, and then took off. This time Mickey leaned forward and let the reins slip through his fingers just enough to give me perfect freedom, and we landed perfectly. He patted my neck as we trotted along the headland and jumped me back over a lower place further down the ditch.

We had many rides together over the common and through Connolly's fields, or trotting slowly along the lanes, between banks matted with dead grass and bramble shoots, dry from the March wind.

Men were busy in the fields, cutting the hedges and burning the trimmings in bonfires that crackled and sent long plumes of pungent smoke drifting across the road.

Heavy horses plodded across the land, drawing the plough through last year's pasture.

Here and there a field was vivid with the young spears of winter-sown wheat, and rooks up in the beech-trees across the road were nesting in a noisy colony. Fat grey pigeons waddled about in pairs under the trees by the roadside.

In April I shed my old dead winter hairs and grew a bright new chestnut coat, and when I trotted out with the van on a sunny morning with the wind whipping my mane it was very good to be alive.

12

Conspiracy

WHEN the days grew longer and April came, there were lambs in the fields that we passed as we jogged along with the van.

They raced along the headlands in bunches, and all day the deep bleat of the ewes answered their shrill maaings.

At evening they drifted across the field, grazing quietly or standing while their lambs fed with wagging tails.

Connolly's lambs were marked with his initials in big black letters on their short woolly fleeces, and round their necks as soon as they were born, he tied a red ribbon to keep away marauding vermin.

Shep lay up in the field at lambing time, on a sack in the lee of the hedge, and with all his precautions, Connolly had lambs killed one night by a stray dog, when he came home late from a fair.

In the warm mild weather the gorse grew yellow along the primrose-studded banks.

One still evening Dan hobbled into the yard on two sticks, he looked much older and very thin.

'That was a shocking crack you got,' said Mickey. 'It was,' Dan growled. 'But sure what could stand up to that tarmac? It's as slippery as glass when it gets a polish with the wind. Why wouldn't they leave a stretch of rough along the edge, instead of thinking of nothing but the cars? It'd break your heart to see your cattle slipping about on a frosty morning, or any other morning for the matter of that. You'd be lucky not to leave a beast on the side of the road with its leg broken.

'There's nothing I hate worse than tarmac, but what do

these city fellers care so long as they have a smooth stretch of road to go boosthering along in their cars? For all they mind, the farmer and the drover and the feller that has to ride the young horses can go hang. It'd sicken you.'

Dan lit his pipe, sucked at it to make it draw, and puffed a curl of blue smoke into the air.

'I don't mind what happens out hunting,' he said. 'That's all the luck of the game and your own look out, but to go and get a good horse destroyed, to say nothing of a broken hip on the roads that are the only way we have for getting about . . . Augh! it'd annoy you.'

He pulled back the bolt of my door and walked in. 'How are the legs holding out, Mickey?' he said.

'Not so bad at all,' said Mickey rather anxiously as he watched Dan feel my legs over from knee to fetlock, and from hock to heel.

'Good enough,' he grunted, 'but there's a splint coming on the near fore.'

I had been feeling sore in my near fore for some days, and there was a small bony lump coming on the cannon-bone.

'Ah well, it's not in a bad place,' said Dan. 'If I were you I'd turn her out for a couple of months. If you give her hard work now you might lay her up altogether, and the splint would be a lot bigger when it was formed.'

Mickey told him how he had learnt to jump, and Dan sat on the remains of the winter log pile and listened. 'That's the way,' he approved, 'it's the way I learnt myself when I was a young one, only my father used to give me a belt of the ashplant across the knuckles if he saw me hanging on to a horse's mouth going over the fences. You need never be afraid to catch hold of the mane, or the neck strap of a martingale if you have one, that's no shame, but to ruin a horse's mouth and his nerve by catching him with the bit every time he goes to throw a lep . . . Don't you ride that

mare in anything but a snaffle. There's more horses ruined
by people who don't know the working of a double bridle
than any other way. It'd sicken you to see the inside of a
horse's mouth after a day's hunting in a double bridle with
people who'd swear they knew how to use it, and they'd
believe they did, too.'

Connolly came into the yard with Shep at his heels, and
Mickey told him about my lameness. 'Sure there's nothing
else to pull the van,' he said. 'What in the divil's name's
wrong with her, Dan?'

Dan told him. 'I know of a good cob going cheap that'd
be the very one for the van,' he said, 'and you might make
a bit on the mare.'

'How's that?' said Connolly. 'Couldn't you sell her as a
boy's hunter?' said Dan. 'Let Mickey here take her out for a
couple of times with the hounds and you'll soon find
a buyer for her. That mare's too good altogether for the
van.'

'She's good enough for me,' said Michael Connolly, who
hated to be hurried into anything. Dan said no more, he
knew his man.

The next time I went out in the trap I was very sore in
front, and went so short that Connolly was forced to agree
that Dan was right. Something had to pull the van, so he
went out the next day and brought back a butty looking
black cob that seemed to have done harness work all his
life.

It was the first of May, and I had just finished growing
my summer coat. Mickey and Shep and I walked down the
road in the warm afternoon, and along the green lane until
we came to the wooden gate of the long field where Connolly's cattle grazed. Leading me through it, Mickey took
my bridle off and turned me loose.

I would not gallop because of my leg but I rolled and
rolled, and grunted and shook myself and rolled again, and

then moved off to crop the sweet young grass, growing round and sleek as the days slid into weeks and May became June.

'Now wasn't it the best of luck her getting that splint?' said Dan, when he came to look at me one day, and he winked at Mickey as they walked away.

13

Out to grass

ONE evening in July it was heavily hot, the leaves of the trees drooped and the cattle panted in the shade. The birds seemed to have vanished, there were none of them in the long field, and the brown butterflies that rose and fell across the meadow, hung with closed wings under the grass stems.

The sun could not shine through the heavy haze that veiled the sky. Through it, the shapes of high piled cloud showed dimly, their summits crested white like waves. The horizon was a dark heavy blue, and the willows rose like smoke against it when in the evening the setting sun flooded the fields with a stormy yellow light.

The great clouds moved slowly across the sky, their flat bases ink blue, and a sudden gust of wind swept through the poplar tree.

As the dusk grew deeper, the dim mass closed slowly over the last patch of clear sky. A blinding flash lit up the whole field, showing the huddled cattle standing under the ash tree, throwing every leaf of it into relief against the coming storm.

For a moment there was silence. Not a bird moved. Then crash after crash of thunder joined horizon to horizon in a terrifying vibration of sound that rolled and retreated and volleyed again.

In the silence that followed, the night was so black that I could not see the grass at my feet. I could hear the wind coming, whistling as it came.

At one moment the air about us was heavily calm, not a leaf stirred, then the wind leaped at us, lashing the branches about in a frenzy of movement. Above the tumult of the wind I could hear the roar of coming rain beating on countless millions of stiff green leaves.

It came in a wall of water driven by the storm, and I tucked my tail in and stood with my ears back, turning my quarters to it as it passed over me.

Flash after flash of lightning lit up the sky, thunder split and crackled, I felt deafened and stunned by the noise of it.

With a last muttering roll of thunder a pale streak of light appeared in the east, and grew wider as the tattered edge of the storm passed over us and rumbled more faintly towards the west.

The wind dropped slowly, the lashing rain came in intermittent showers, grew light and more friendly and ceased.

In the stillness I could hear the patter of drops running off the leaves on to the grass and the rush of flood water racing down the newly filled river.

A smell of hot wet earth and drenched grasses rose on the air, and a corncrake called anxiously from the other side of the flattened meadow.

In the clear night one star twinkled, and I moved forward, shaking the water out of my mane, and began to eat.

After the storm there came a week of fine sunny weather, and Mickey came across my field with a scythe, and cut all round the meadow, clearing a path several metres wide between the tall waving grasses that had a soft purple bloom on their heads, and the overgrown darker greenness of the bramble and blackthorn hedge that stood at the edge of the headland, its feet buried in meadowsweet, and hemlock, and robin-run-the-hedge.

Early the next morning, two borrowed horses pulled the mowing machine clattering down the lane and through the gate of the meadow, and hour after hour the machine whirred and clacked as the horses walked round and round. Stopping at the headland to their driver's 'Woa', backing as he cried 'Hike! Hike!' and starting off again down the other side of the square as he called 'Come up now' to their tossing heads.

The square of standing grass grew smaller at each turn and the neat swathes lay in long overlapping lines, silvery green in the sunlight.

The air hummed with the whirr of mowing machines in the neighbouring meadows where rooks and gulls flew and hovered over the swathes, and the air was heavy with the smell of hot, new mown hay.

When, in the evening, the square had dwindled to a narrow strip from which a few scared rabbits bolted and fled, and a corncrake hustled her black fluffy brood to the shelter of the hedge, the two great horses drew the knife across the last remaining ribbon of meadow, and levelled it flat. Then they turned and pulled the machine out of the gate, rattling away up the lane to their home farm for the night.

For a day or two, the hay lay drying in the hot sun, and towards the middle of the week, Mickey came into my field with the cart bridle. I stood still while he put it on and he led me along the road to the yard where I had not been for two long idle months. My splint was set now, and I was as sound as ever.

Tommy, the cob, had just come in with the van and whinnied a greeting to me over the gate of the paddock.

I was harnessed to the swathe turner and we rattled down the lane to the meadow.

Mickey pulled the lever, and the revolving teeth of the machine tossed the hay so that the green underside of the swathe was turned and dried in the sun. We went down the side of the field till we came to the end of the swathe following the track of the mowing machine.

It was very hot and I kept tossing my head at the flies which hummed in a cloud around us watching their opportunity to settle on my hide.

We tossed hay all day and I was tired and glad to be unharnessed in the evening and turned into my field again.

I rolled on the grass, rubbing my neck and back against the earth, rolling from one side to the other. Then I got up with a grunt, shook myself, and went thirstily down to the water to drink, stirring up streamers of mud with my hooves among the shining ripples.

The next day I was brought up to the yard early. Tommy was harnessed to an iron hay-rake and I followed him down to the meadow with a flat wooden pronged rake with two handles; it scooped up the rows of hay that Tommy released from his iron horse-rake, and brought piles of it to the men who tossed it into high cocks with their pitchforks.

With a twist of the wooden handle, the hay slid off the rake and the men tossed it up on to the cock while I went for more.

Soon there was a row of cocks from one end of the field to the other as the men worked in their shirt-sleeves.

Shep lay by a coat in the middle of the field, and at lunch hour Mickey and his father ate their sandwiches in the shade of a haycock while Tommy and I, unhitched from the rakes, grazed along the tangled headland.

By the end of the day we had finished the field.

After the haymaking there was no work for me to do for nearly a fortnight. The weather which had been hot and sunny, changed suddenly. Drifting masses of dirty grey cloud blew up from the north west, and a cold wind swept transparent veils of rain across the fields.

My coat was waterproof with grease and accumulated

waste thrown off by my skin, so that I did not mind a wetting.

My mane lay dank and damp on my neck, and the grass was heavy and grey with moisture.

Except when I was feeding. I stood under the trees with my back to the wind and listened to the water dripping dismally off the leaves.

The whole countryside was dark green and grey. Grey clouds, grey rain, and dull green leaves.

Then one evening the rain stopped, a long bar of light sky, yellow and pale grew along the west. Slowly the edge of torn, dark cloud moved across the sky, leaving behind it an ever widening space of watery blue.

Shafts of light shone down like fingers from the hidden sun, bathing the trees in yellow stormy light and turning to silver the wind-blown leaves of the poplar by the gate.

As the last line of cloud rolled eastward, the sun came out, full and warm, and drew up to it the smell of rain-drenched earth and meadowsweet, and heavy flowering grasses. Steam rose from the cows' backs, and from my own wet hide as I grazed, moving slowly forward through the sunlight.

There were red poppies in the cornfield next to the meadow, and in the days of hot sun that followed the rain, the thick waving carpet of oats, stand three feet high, turned from green to yellow and from yellow to ripe gold.

Ripples ran across it when the wind blew and the heads rustled together with a soft brushing sound.

A vixen and her cubs lived among the tall stalks, and made long narrow passages from the hedges to the beaten-down hollow with high golden walls where they had lived since they left the breeding earth. In the evening the cubs played on the bank of my field, rolling each other over, fighting and biting and snarling at each other in mock warfare, while the dog and the vixen sat on their quarters and watched them.

The cubs were already losing their woolly coats and the faces that were curiously like a young lamb's, and were growing sharp of nose and wary-eyed.

The vixen took them hunting for mice in the long grass, they were leggy and lank, and their brushes were not so full as the old fox's.

At sunrise the dog fox passed me, trotting home along the hedge, his brush just clearing the dewy grass.

Earlier in the summer, when the cubs were in the breeding earth in the double ditch that bounded one side of my field, Mickey had walked over at twilight to see if the cubs were using the earth that year.

While he was down in the ditch, the dog and the vixen returned, trotting side by side through the grasses, and Mickey met them face to face as he reappeared.

They stopped dead, their pointed ears sharply upright on each side of their triangular faces, and as the dog fox turned and galloped away the vixen leaped into the air with open mouth, and her weird cry split the evening air. Again and again she yelled, galloping towards the headland, a cry like a view halloa, ear-piercing and startling in the stillness.

Mickey startled, stood for a moment watching her, and she turned and came through the grass, throwing back her head and holloaing with wide open mouth.

He watched her for a second, then grinned and walked away across the field, while the vixen stood up in the grass and looked after him, yelling as he went. At the gate he turned and shouted to her. 'I'll be doing the holloaing next year,' he cried.

Soon there was work for me to do, for all our hay was out in the field in rows of high cocks standing in the after-grass.

Connolly hired two horses and borrowed bogies, as the long flat wooden slides on round iron wheels are called.

I was harnessed to one of them, and early in the morning we drove out of the yard and rattled down the lane to the hay field.

Connolly and two of the boys drove the bogies, and old Dan and another man waited with pitchforks in the yard to throw the hay up into the barn as we brought the cocks in.

The empty bogies were light and the wide iron wheels made a terrific noise on the rough lane. It was the school holidays, and every bogie carried its load of laughing, squealing children.

It was hard to sit on the bouncing, slippery slide. Their teeth rattled in their heads and they held tightly on to the big hay rope. The bolder ones hung their legs over the sides and held nothing at all.

Sometimes they fell off and had to run to catch up but it was all part of the fun.

Mickey drove my bogie, standing up like a charioteer and balancing there somehow.

We trotted up the field in line, to the head of the first row. One bogie to each of the three cocks. The children scrambled off and we were turned and backed so that the end of the bogies came next to the cock.

Then a pin was drawn and the end of the bogie was lowered to the ground. 'Hike,' said Mickey, and I threw myself back on my hocks against the shaft, running the end of the bogie in under the cock.

There was a pulley with a handle lying across the top of the bogie, two ropes were unwound from it and passed round the back of the cock. Each had a big iron clasp, and when they were fastened together, Mickey put the handle in the pulley and wound slowly for the cock was heavy.

Squeak, squeak went the handle, and slowly the cock slid up the bogie to the top. When the edge of it reached the pulley, Mickey said 'Come up' to me, and I threw my weight against the collar so that the weight of the cock raised the back of the bogie off the ground, and it clicked into position.

When it was level, a strong rope was passed from the back of the bogie over the top of the cock, and fastened at the bottom of the shaft.

There was hardly room for Mickey to stand, so he had to balance with both feet on the shaft and his back pressed against the hay.

The children were not supposed to ride on the loaded bogies for fear of the cock slipping and because of the weight on the horse, so they ran behind, scrambling up on the ledge at the back of the cock when no one was looking.

Michael Connolly roared at them when he caught them doing this, and they scattered like chickens, to cluster back again the next moment.

When we got back to the barn, pulling and hauling, the bogies were tipped up, we threw our weight into our collars, and the cocks slid off. Then Dan and his partner, one on the rick and one below, set to work with their pitchforks; one man throwing up the hay and the other catching it and tossing it into place, till at evening the barn was piled high with sweet smelling old meadow hay, and Dan had to stand on the top of it and trample it down while the other man threw it up to him.

I was tired when Mickey led me down to my field, and the stream washed coolly round my fetlocks as I drank long delicious draughts in the shallows.

I rolled and shook myself and began to graze with that deep enjoyment of comfort that only hard work of muscle and sinew brings when it is time to relax and be at ease again.

14
Harvest

In August, when the evenings were beginning to shorten, the whirr of the reapers hummed over the fields.

There was yellow wheat in the field next to mine, and all one long sunny day two great bay horses pulled the reaper and binder round and round a narrowing square of waving grain.

Men, women, and children followed in line, stooking the sheaves till the field was dotted with rows of stooks, and the lunch hour came.

Then they all sat down in the shade of a stook, to beer and sandwiches and cans of tea. The men smoked their pipes and the children played with the collie dogs.

The horses, unharnessed, shook themselves and grazed along by the hedge.

They were such friends, those two, that they even grazed as if they were in double harness, moving forward side by side to crop the long green grass.

In the evening there was only a small square left in the middle of the field, and the collie dogs stood with their ears forward waiting.

A corncrake stole out of the wheat and ran furtively through the stooks, her young ones following her.

Little brown mice with beady eyes ran helter skelter to the nearest refuge. A pheasant rose with a flurry of whirring wings and rocketed over the hedge. And then like brown bombs the rabbits burst from covert, bounding across the stubble with white scuts bobbing.

The dogs flew in pursuit, the men shouted, the children ran. Many were killed and others got away. The dead rabbits were thrown in a heap and divided among the men. They were very numerous that year and the inroads that they made among the crops were a big loss to the farmers.

There were two or three hundred rabbits in my ditch alone, and they fouled the grazing for a long way into the field.

Later a plague came among the overcrowded burrows and the rabbits died in scores. Only the strongest survived.

At last the wheat was cut, the last sheaf stooked. The men threw their coats on their shoulders and walked home behind their horses.

Later when the moon rose, the stooks threw long shadows on the ground and little field mice ran bewilderedly through the stubble looking for their wrecked home. None the wiser, though for centuries this thing had happened to them, they built new ones in the stooks.

A rat, looking for its wrecked tunnel and naked pink young ones that a puppy had unearthed rose on its hind legs with a vicious squeal. As on silent wings a white-faced barn owl drifted down to it and bore it swiftly away.

One Sunday afternoon, Connolly and Dan walked down to my field with the collie dog and stood looking at me for a long while.

'It's this way, Michael,' said Dan. 'You can pick up a pony any day that'll pull the van and do the bit of work on the farm, but this mare has the makings of a good thing in her, and you were damn lucky to get her so cheap.

'The bit of work she's done'll do her no harm, but take my tip and don't use her any more on the road. Let young Mickey take her out with the Harriers and we'll see what sort she is.

'I was watching her galloping round the field the other

day, and says I to myself, if she was mine I'd be picking up cobs' races with her.

'She's too good altogether to be battering around in the van and Mickey's heart is with the horses.

'Now I've known you since we mitched school together, Michael, and you'll not take offence. Let the lad follow the hunt on the mare if he wants to, it'll make a rider of him and if he has the stuff in him we'll see him coming past the post at Punchestown on a good horse one of these days.

'We'll say nothing, and we'll be in on this together, and school the mare for the point-to-points in the spring. You never know but we might pull off ten to one on her. Will you do it, Mike?'

Connolly drew lines with his stick on the grass and thought for a while.

'I never was much of a one for horses,' he said, 'but maybe you're right, Dan. I'll bring her in and feed her and Mickey can hunt her provided he doesn't skip his work. You'll have to see to the schooling and training, and we'll be in on it together.'

They turned to go away and I watched them close the wooden gate and walk up the brown lane with their hands behind their backs, Connolly's black bowler tilted over his nose and Dan's black pipe puffing blue smoke into the September sunlight.

Mist was rising off the aftergrass in the evenings. Already it was growing colder and skies were flaming at sunset with a hint of coming frost.

The grass was beginning to lose its flavour and the sap to sink in the trees. My summer coat was loosening for Autumn was in the air and dahlias bloomed in front of cottage gardens. It was time that I came up off grass.

The next morning I heard steps in the lane, and presently Mickey's small red head and snub-nosed freckled face appeared above the wooden gate of my field.

He had a head-collar in his hand, and Shep trotted in front of him waving his tail.

Usually I gave him a nicker of welcome and trotted to meet him, and he would pat my neck, and rub my head between the ears. Sometimes he gave me a handful of dandelions, but this morning I thought I would have some fun.

I trotted towards him, stepping out proudly, swinging along with my head and tail up and mane flying. 'Come along, the girl,' he called, holding out his hand.

I circled round him and then stood still, threw up my head, and snorted very loudly.

'Woa, the girl,' said Mickey, and stretched out his hand to me. I stretched out my nose and touched it, squealed, whipped round, threw up my heels and galloped round the field.

Faster and faster I flew, my hooves drumming on the hard earth, my mane and tail flying. I swung my head from side to side and then bucked, arching my back, my head between my forelegs and every muscle taut. It was a lovely feeling and I did it again for pure joy. Then I stopped dead and stood with my ears forward, waiting for Mickey to come up to me.

'You're very full of yourself this morning,' he said.

I let him get nearly close enough to put a hand on my mane, then wheeled away, coming back to him with nose outstretched but not quite close enough for him to catch me. It was a grand game.

Shep watched us with his ears forward, his tongue running out, waving his plumy tail and laughing.

I put back my ears and bounded at him, leaping high into the air and bringing my forefeet down close to his back as he slid out of the way and barked at me. Mickey shouted a warning, but I would not have hurt him, it was all in fun.

The stream ran into a pond in the corner of the field, and I let Mickey follow me up into the corner.

He thought he had me, but this was the best part of the game. I snorted at him, walked into the pond and began splashing myself all over with my forefoot.

Mud and water flew in showers as I pawed, bowing my head, and wetting Mickey who stood on the bank. Cool water ran down my legs and tickled my flanks. The pond was cloudy where I stirred up the mud. 'You villain,' said Mickey, 'Come out of that.'

When I was tired of it I came out and walked up to him, letting him catch me and put the head-collar on. We walked out of the field, down the lane into the road and presently turned through the gate into the yard.

My stable door was open and I snorted and walked inside. There was fresh straw on the floor and a bucket of water stood in the corner.

I sniffed all round and pawed at the straw till my hoof thudded on the cobbles underneath. Through the crack in the boards of the partition I heard a chain clank and the cow stirred uneasily.

I whipped round and stuck my head out over the half door, looking across the yard to the river and the familiar fields beyond.

Some children were running barefoot along the bank with a stick for a fishing rod and a jar of water for the pinkeens they hoped to catch.

The big rooster stood up on the manure heap and flapped his wings loudly, crowing a challenge to the Rhode Island cockerel across the way. His hens clucked and scratched and dusted themselves in the sun below the wall.

The September sky was a paler, frosty blue, behind the dark green of the elm trees that were already tinged with yellow, and the air had a freshness and a smell of coming autumn. The Hunting Season was at hand, and all through the country horses were being brought up off grass.

15

The September hunt

WHILE the beech trees were still dark with the dull green of early Autumn, Mickey and I went cub hunting one September morning.

As we jogged through bramble lanes in the half light, our hooves made hollow splashing noises in the muddy puddles.

Dan rode with us on a brown four-year-old, and presently the sun came up on a misty world of grass, blue grey under its heavy coat of dew, and filmy hangings of spiders' webs that spread from bush to bush holding millions of sparkling drops towards the rising sun.

A robin sang in the loops of bramble by the roadside as we dropped downhill past a narrow glen whose banks were ragged with gorse and ash saplings. I could hear the voice of the rushing stream that ran along the bottom of the glen, under the overhanging bushes.

At the top of the hill, the fields spread away, fenced with wide ditches and ragged thorn hedges planted here and there with trees that grew wherever the wind had sown them, or the slash hook had spared their sapling growth.

From scattered cottages along the road, smoke rose straight and blue into the morning air, and perhaps a mile away lay a long line of fir woods behind a grey demesne wall.

We had pulled up to a walk at the foot of the rise and the silence of the fields was unbroken, save for the steady clippit-cloppit-clippit-cloppit of four pairs of hooves.

Suddenly I heard something and threw my head up. 'Whist,' said Dan, and we stopped dead. My heart began to pound between my ribs with excitement so that I could hear it beating. It was the cry of hounds. They were hunting in the wood behind the grey wall and their voices came to us like clashing bells.

'Begob, they're hunting,' said Dan. 'Hold on now till we see if they come this way.' As he spoke, a white speck topped the wall and dropped down, it was the leading hound, and the pack came over behind it in a wave and slid across the green of the intervening fields.

We were too far off to see them clearly, they were vague black dots with spidery legs and here and there a patch of white, but their cry came up to us on the thin still air, and they were coming our way.

Suddenly there was silence, the black dots bunched, spread out and scattered along the line of the hedge and into the next field. Then the voice of a single hound spoke in the stillness, the pack flew to it, and giving tongue again they swept towards us, leaping the ditches and scrambling through the gaps in the brambly hedges that lay in their path.

Behind them, a small pink dot appeared, then another and another. Four dark dots followed them and they came quickly along the line that the pack had taken.

By this time I was dancing with excitement and snatching at my bit. Dan's young horse stood like a rock with ears cocked forward and his eyes on the advancing pack. 'I see him, Dan! I see him,' said Mickey, clutching Dan's arm. 'Over beyond the two ash trees.'

'Be quiet then, and don't say a word now,' said Dan. 'And stand close into the hedge.'

Looking over the tops of the brambles, I could see the fox coming up the field.

He was loping along, going steadily, with his ears pricked forward and his bushy white tagged brush straight out behind him. A big red roan fox with a white throat and very black ears. He made straight for the corner and disappeared through the fence with a whisk of his brush.

'That's a fresh-looking fox,' said Dan. 'That feller'd lift a calf, he's the size of a wolf.'

Ahead of the pack a bunch of cattle were running, and in a gap between two fields they checked again. They spread out, casting here and there, while the cattle, well across the line, wheeled to watch them, bucking and bellowing.

Presently the pack got their heads up and stood baffled, watching the huntsman as he came galloping up the field on a big brown horse.

The other horses pulled up and stood looking on.

'This is just where we oughtn't to be,' said Dan. 'I suppose this is what John Toomey calls cub hunting!'

He put his finger to his ear and gave a piercing yell, then jumping his young horse through a gap in the fence, he cleared the ditch and galloping over the field, held up his cap where the fox had gone out of it at the corner of the fence.

The huntsman blew his horn. The whip put the pack on to him and he came galloping up the field with his hounds.

'Where'd he go?' he shouted to Dan. 'Here in the corner,' said Dan, showing him the place with his cap.

A hound picked up the line as they came to the fence. 'Forrard, forrard, forrard,' cried John Toomey, his lean face scarlet under his black cap.

'Come on, Christy, open the gate for me, 'he called to his first whip who jumped off his horse and dragged the heavy wooden gate to one side.

'Last man shuts it,' called the Master, an elderly man in a tweed coat, on a good-looking bay.

The hounds came over the road, scrambled whimpering

through the hedge and launched themselves down hill as John Toomey clattered through.

Christy swung himself on to his horse, and five other riders came galloping up. A young man in a tweed coat, a girl riding side-saddle on a chestnut horse, a big burly man with a bowler hat on the back of his head and his wide white face scratched from ear to chin, and two others.

There were leaves in their horses' manes and on their coats, torn from the brambles in the fences they had left behind.

They clattered into the lane as the second whip galloped up and stopped to close the gate. 'Come on, Mickey,' said Dan, and we followed them as they clattered through a farmyard and down the wide field.

The pack were flying down the slope of the hill, charging the banks and flying the ditches as they came to them. And a flock of sheep wheeled in a panic from their path and fled with bobbing tails.

We jumped a wide ditch in a corner, behind Dan. Leave her head alone,' he flung back to Mickey. 'Grab the saddle or anything else you like,' and Mickey gave me my head at every fence.

In front of us the backs of the other riders rose and fell over the green banks, and the quarters of their horses loomed large as they swung over the blind ditches where brambles masked the brown depth.

Dan's young horse was going solemnly and carefully, he liked to see what he was jumping. Mickey's cap fell off, swept away by a branch, but he let it lie. Several times he was nearly off, and as we dropped down into a lane, over a blind ditch, I swung sharply to the right, after Dan's horse and he went out over my shoulder.

Dan caught my rein as I came past his leg. 'Didn't I tell you to stick your knees in?' he said. 'Hop up now, hop up.'

'So I did, but she went away from under me,' said Mickey hopping on one toe as he grabbed for the stirrup.

'Hold on now or you'll never make a Jock,' said Dan as we clattered down the lane and jumped out into the field through gnarled old thorn bushes and over a blind ditch.

The young man in the tweed coat turned his horse to the right and we followed him. Hounds were running right handed three fields ahead, and at the bottom of the field a stream ran, with tussocks of rushes growing along it.

The man put his horse at it and as they landed, the rotten bank gave way, and the horse dropped his hind legs, rolling over on to his side.

The rider scrambled to one side and pulled it to its feet again.

'Are you all right Mr Scott?' called Dan as he pulled up.

'Yes, I'm all right thanks, go ahead,' came the answer, as Bill Scott vaulted back into the saddle.

'We'll go this way,' said Dan and galloped down to the corner of the field where, masked by overhanging branches, there was a cattle pass into the next field.

We scrambled through, with Mickey's head low on my neck and there in front of us was Bill Scott on his roan mare, striding down the field with the pack running along the headland to the left of them.

Two fields to the right, the gleam of flying colour showed where John Toomey and his whips were topping a bank, and we dropped down into a brown rushy snipe bog, where the hounds rose and fell as they leaped the high rushes.

'Cut the wire, Tony,' John Toomey cried as he came to the edge of the river that bounded it. We swung along the bank and jumped a small ditch into the same field with him.

Tony, the second whip, was off his horse cutting the

T–D

wire with wire cutters. It parted with a twang and a jangle
as the loose wire coiled back on itself and looped round the
post.

John Toomey's horse plunged down into the muddy
depth and wallowed across, heaving itself up the bank
with a splash and a scramble.

Little brown birds rose from the rushes and twittered
anxiously overhead.

'You go on, Colonel Scott,' said the burly man to his
grey-haired neighbour who was the Master of the pack.
One by one they dropped down into the water and cantered on over the bog.

It was hot now and I was far from fit. I was beginning to
feel tired in spite of the excitement of the run. Although
Dan had not hustled his young horse, and hounds had been
hunting slowly most of the time, we had come a long
way.

The going was hard in spite of the recent rain and my
legs welcomed the cool swirl of the water and the feel of it
on my flanks.

The other horses were dark with sweat, and their riders'
faces were scarlet.

'Easy now,' said Dan, and we trotted across the bog,
watching the horses in front of us as they picked their way
over the small bog drains and hummocks that were still
hard from the summer's drought.

A small pink flower dotted the patches of grass, and the
smell of mint and crushed bog myrtle was heavy where the
horses had trodden.

Ahead of us rose a rough gorse-clad hill crowned by
Scotch fir trees. Tangles of bramble and rough grass fought
with the ragged gorse on its steep flanks, and towards it the
hounds were flinging themselves, crying like seagulls.

The three red coats galloping through the bog were vivid
colour against the browns and greens of gorse and rushes

as they made their way along the top of a bank that ran like a causeway towards the foot of the hill.

Behind them followed Bill Scott and his father. 'That's Jack Burney,' said Dan to Mickey as the burly man cantered ahead of us, his great shoulders almost bursting the cloth coat he wore. 'There isn't a fence in the country he wouldn't jump. In or over he'd try them all, and he must ride nearly sixteen stone. God help the horse that would try and refuse with him, he's a terrible man to go.'

'Ah Dan, go on! go on!' said Mickey. 'Sure the hounds are the length of the bog away from us.'

'Do you want to kill the horses?' said Dan. 'They'll be in that old thicket of brambles for half an hour or more if they don't get him now.'

He pulled up his horse to a walk and looked back at me. 'Speedy stuck it well,' he said. 'Did you like it, Mick?'

'Oh Dan, it was grand!' said Mickey.

The hounds had flung themselves into the covert as we pulled up below the hill, clouds of midges rose and settled on us as we stamped and fidgeted, shaking our heads and swishing our tails at the pests.

'That wouldn't be bad for the middle of the season, Bill,' said the girl to Bill Scott. 'A great hunt, Polly,' he said. 'I thought my last hour had come over some of those blind ditches,' she said, turning to Jack Burney.

'Sure Marcus would jump them blindfold, Mrs McCalmont.' he said with a grin.

'That was a great hunt altogether.' He turned his horse round and looked at me. 'That's a good little mare you have,' he said to Mickey.

A cock pheasant rocketed up out of the brambles and sailed on curved wings across the bog. Brown rabbits dashed out of the bushes with bobbing tails, and seeing us, dashed back again.

John Toomey was up on the hill with his hounds and

Tony, Bill Scott, and Christy were watching the covert at different points.

The whole landscape seemed to be swimming in golden sunlight; it was a perfect September morning.

The cry of hounds raged round the hillside, gorse bushes swayed and blackbirds fled shrieking to a safer refuge. Suddenly there was a snarling tussle among the gorse.

'Whoo, Whoop!' called John Toomey. Christy and Tony came galloping round the cover and flung their reins to Dan and Mickey. I put my ears back at Tony's horse as it rubbed its head against my shoulder.

We all moved round the hillside and there, at the foot of an old stone quarry stood John Toomey with his hounds about him. They had broken up their fox and proudly one old hound trotted away with the mask held in his teeth, he would carry it with him as the pack jogged home.

Some of the hounds rolled on the grass, two of them bristled up to each other, stiff-legged and warming for a fight.

'Come along then, come along,' called John Toomey.

'Get along. Whoop,' said Tony, cracking his whip.

The horn called long and mournfully to a missing hound as we jogged along the green bank that wound across the rushes to the fields that curved round the bog, and the bramble-sided lane that led us home.

16

The opening day

On a fine frosty November morning we jogged along the winding lane that came out at the little village of Roscannon where hounds were to meet at eleven o'clock.

Roscannon was about twelve miles from home, but we met the hounds coming down to the covert which was on our side of the village.

I heard the dull drumming of hooves on the road as we jogged slowly along and I pricked my ears to it and began to dance. Above the clatter I could hear people's voices, sharp and clear on the frosty air. Then a pink coat appeared through a gap in the hedge, and another and another, and the field came jogging along the road behind Christy who rode in front of the pack on his short-tailed grey.

John Toomey rode in the middle of the hounds and they waved their sterns, looking up at his horse.

Tony, riding the Captain, a sour old blood horse with a nappy temper, gave Mickey a grin as we pulled into the side of the road to let them pass. And we followed the field through a wooden farm gate into a long piece of land, full of pale golden rushes, where some of the young horses started bucking and squealing with excitement.

The pink coats, the hounds, and the bright-skinned horses shining with grooming and condition, made lovely patches of colour as they brushed through the rushes, and squelched across wet bog.

Snipe rose with a screech and a flash of white underside as they zigzagged away and the field spread out to jump a drain that ran across the land to the covert fence.

Roscannon covert is full of thorns and trees and flaming scarlet dogwood along the side of a slope, and it nearly always holds. If a fox breaks to the left you may go straight out over a blind drop into rushy bog and down to the double with a line of crooked beech trees along the top. Or, if he breaks on the other side, you must push through a cattle gap in the hedge, over a little stream and up a steep slope to the fields that lie towards the grey town by the main road, and either way you must gallop to catch them.

That day, as we waited in the frosty sunlight, our breath making smoke on the air, the whistle shrilled, almost as hounds opened, Tony's ear-splitting holloa speeded the fox away over long bare fields to the thick blackthorn depths of Moloney's covert, and he went as straight as a dart.

There was crushing at the cattle gap, but we scrambled clear at last and Mickey drove me forward as fast as my chestnut legs would flash, and they were working like pistons.

We made for a gap in the first fence and jumped out over a drop ditch between two twisty thorn trees, landing clean out over the wide place into the next field, as Jack Burney and Polly McCalmont landed on either side of us. Hounds were just two fields ahead and running hard.

John Toomey was close on the left, and Jack Burney on his big blood horse was standing up in his stirrups with his hat pushed on to the back of his head as he thundered down to the next fence, a wide ditch, its deep sides matted with dead yellow grass.

The wind sang round my ears, I saw the shoes of Jack Burney's horse flash as he rose and sailed over, and then, at the full stretch of my body, I shot over after him, flying through the air to land well out on the far side. 'Steady now, young feller,' warned Tony, as we galloped down to the great grassy double with a few Scotch fir trees along the top.

The horse in front of me fell on the far side and I had to do it from a standstill. As I landed, Mickey lost his balance and pulled my head up. For a moment I staggered backwards with my forelegs pawing the air, and then by a gigantic effort of muscle I righted myself and him and got over safely. 'Be damn! that's a good cob!' I heard a man say.

The pack had checked a little farther on and we stood in a corner of the headland, steaming, while John Toomey cast them. They jogged round the field in front of his horse, heads down, nosing everywhere, their sterns feathering.

A little tan and white bitch lingered by the yellow sunlit double where the fir trees were tossing a little in the light breeze.

Presently she whimpered and the pack came racing to her. 'Forrard to Garnish! Forrard! Forrard! Forrard!' cried John Toomey as they raced down the headland.

There was a gate beside the loose stone wall into a little wood, and as everyone was crowding through it, Mickey put me at the wall.

I jumped very high as I was afraid of knocking my legs against the top of it and Mickey flew into the air like a rocket. His reins went one way, his irons another, and feeling a welcome lightness about my back, I shot out over the next ditch and raced after the flying pack, pulling up with a snort in a farmyard where my iron shoes struck bright sparks from the cobbles.

Horses passed me, clattering through the yard, steam from their sweating hides was blown on the wind, the cry of the pack faded and ceased, and the last sound of hoofbeats grew further away.

Far down the field I saw a figure running. It was Mickey, he was wiping a bloody nose with the back of his hand.

'Bad luck to you, Speedy,' he said, as he scrambled up. 'Will you gallop like hell now till we catch them.'

When we saw hounds again they had killed their fox and were drawing Moloney's covert.

We stood on a windy rise of the land where we could look down and see a pink coat at each end of the square of brown thorn bushes and tall fir trees, where Tony and Christy were watching close to the ragged hedge so that the fox should not see them.

All round me horses were standing, with their manes lifted by the light wind. Every head was turned towards the covert, and every ear pricked forward. But the covert was blank and John Toomey called his hounds out with a long mournful note on his horn.

They came jogging quietly up towards us and we turned away to the brown beech trees on the slope beside Cloneen where we were going.

The straggling field fell into line behind the hounds, and the red and black coats rose and fell for a long way down the lane. As they turned the corner I could see the line of hats bobbing along the hedge, from the velvet caps with the pack, through the lines of tall hats and bowlers, to the torn cloth cap of the rough rider on the last of the wild young horses, at the tail of the field, where the bicycles and a few motor cars began.

17

The evening run

In November and December we had some good days with the Cloneen hounds and with the Harriers that hunted the country near our village.

I leaned to know when Mickey was going hunting, he would feed me earlier in the morning, and then I would dance and curtsey out of the yard, and shy at all the stone heaps on the road, out of pure excitement and lightness of heart.

Mickey was as keen as I was. I think he was never so happy as when we were hunting together, and the end of December saw us hacking towards Clonaney covert which was the last draw at the end of a frosty day.

There weren't very many people left, only about ten of the regulars who never went home till the hounds did, unless their horses had had enough.

Clonaney had not been drawn for two years, and we never expected it to hold as it was so close to the village.

The long Clonaney lane was deep in half-frozen mud and it was very cold in the rushy field outside the green patch of gorse.

I stood where I could see up the ride that runs across the middle of the covert, and listened to the bits jingling and the horses shifting about.

The afternoon was very still with the coming frost, and Mickey ran his hand up and down my mane and blew on his fingers to keep them warm.

John Toomey was at the far end of the covert crying, 'Yoi, try there,' and 'Leu troi for 'im . . . Leu troi . . . Yoi, push 'im out there.' Tony was standing up in his stirrups in the middle of the ride, turning his head from side to side so as to see the fox whichever way he crossed. His pink coat glowed among the gorse against the cold blue sky.

'Swish!' A big lean fox bounded across the ride. 'Over! Over!' said Tony to John Toomey, and cracked his whip.

The hounds came leaping over the loops of bramble. 'Whrrrrrrilllllll' went the whistle from the covert end where Christy had seen the fox go away. I saw it go racing down the hill, followed by a loud holloa, and the pack came scrambling over the covert ditch.

John Toomey cheered them on as they picked up the line, and as they raced across the next field the horses leaped forward with a thunder of flying hooves.

Away we darted, to get a good start. Swish! We went over the first ditch. Tony, ahead of me, fell at the next one, a wide ditch with blackthorn stumps on the take-off side, and Mickey rode me down at it, and over a narrow-back on to the lane where hounds had checked.

Only for a moment they feathered along the lane, scrambled over the bank into the next field, then a big tan and white hound with a deep voice picked up the line along the headland and the pack slid across the field.

I was going steadily to the right of the tail hounds and about half a field behind them, galloping over the grass with long even strides. Fields and fences followed each other and were forgotten. I had eyes only for the fifteen and a half couple of tan and white hounds that were running fast across the next field, flinging themselves over the narrowest part of the ditch where the fox had crossed, and throwing their music back along the frosty air. I hardly noticed the changing outlines of the fields and fences and the rise and fall of the land. Always it was the next fence that held my attention, and the flying pack beyond it.

Then, as we galloped down to the river, taking the great grassy doubles, five of us together, with a spring, a lightning change of feet and a bound and drop over the big ditch on the other side, I saw Bill Scott, galloping ahead of me on his big roan mare, turn a little to the left, and put her at the stream where the take-off looked firm and the landing was less boggy than it was directly in front of us.

The river was deep and wide and there was a strand of wire on the take-off side which the low sun made invisible against the yellow-green grass of the field beyond.

The mare was going fast at it, with the push of the slope behind her, and for one awful moment she seemed to stand completely on her head against the huge red setting sun.

. I had a glimpse of her roan belly and hind legs flying upwards as she turned head over heels, and hitting the far bank, slid down with a splash into the muddy water.

Bill was flung out over her head into the field, and lay, a bright scarlet splash against the grass.

He raised his arm slowly and let it drop again, lying still.

Christy jumped off his horse and ran to him, and the few horses that were there stood and steamed in a group, their riders talking anxiously.

Presently Bill sat up, shook his head with a grin and looked about for the mare. She was none the worse except for a wire scratch on her foreleg.

Bill limped up to her, 'Well, I broke the wire for you, anyway,' he said. 'Give me a leg-up, Christy.'

We could hear the cry of the pack coming over the fields towards the gorsy ridge that runs up to the tower of Cloneen. It faded away for a moment and then broke out again in a clamour of hound voices, each hound chiming in a little behind its neighbour in a medley of sound.

'They must be close to him now,' said John Toomey, putting his horse down the deep drop. He landed with a wallow in the water and plunged up the other side.

Polly McCalmont, Jack Burney, Tony, and a priest on a big blood chestnut followed, and I came behind them, sliding down the drop on my hocks and scrambling up the grassy bank, dripping water and kicking down lumps of earth.

We galloped away into the evening over the long fields, straight into the face of the low sun, taking our fences at a slant because it dazzled us.

Almost in darkness we saw the dim mass of the next covert, a round clump of high beech trees with laurels underneath them, and a mist-wreathed rushy bog beyond. On our left crouched an old deserted house, with high gables and blank sightless windows brooding in the winter dusk.

Hounds were running hard now. They were running to view. I could see the fox, loping down the field, straining every nerve to reach his earth.

Warning almost had him. He dodged like a hare as they coursed him, twisting his brush from side to side. Stylish made a grab at him and missed. He was in the ditch, he was over and into the laurels as the body of the pack crashed through after him.

As we pulled up, steaming in the old stone gateway between the two fields, the cry of the pack had ceased. They were working in the laurels now and somehow they had lost their fox.

Away over the rushy bog a thin mist was rising, and the boles of the beech trees, green about the knees with moss, rose above our heads, their interlacing branches black against the sky. Their great twisted shapes stood in line along the sunk fence and between them Tony stood up in his stirrups and watched the covert ditch.

The gathering night that had stolen the colour from horse and rider had painted the sky a clear pale primrose, and the green of a starling's egg.

Against it, every blackened silhouette possessed a corona of golden light as the sun does in eclipse. Tree and branch and laurel leaf were transformed into weird black twisted shapes, while the sun hung on the rim of the earth, hesitating to slip into outer blackness, as a swimmer does at the edge of a cold, dark pool.

In the dimness of the laurels, blackbirds screeched and fluttered.

'He must be down your end, Tony,' called John Toomey from the other side of the covert. 'They were right on top of him.'

'If so he's got in,' Tony called back. His horse blew through its nose and tossed its head with a jingle of the bit. Suddenly hounds gave tongue. There was a crashing in the laurels and a blackbird shrieked and flashed between the trees. Across the little wood came the deep bay of hounds that have marked to ground.

'Whoo, Whoop!' shouted Tony putting his hand to his ear, and throwing the Captain's reins to Mickey, he leaped down over the covert ditch and waded into the laurels.

'He's in the old earth,' he called to John Toomey.

Christy came cantering along the side of the fence. 'There is a fresh fox gone away the other side,' he said. 'Let him go,' said John Toomey, and he blew his horn softly, calling his hounds away from the earth.

'Come along, Whoop!' cried Tony, wading out of the laurels with the pack leaping after him.

The horn was still calling to lost hounds as we rode away over the top of the hill, by the grey tower of cloneen, with the tired pack jogging at the horses' heels.

They were bunched together behind Christy's horse with their heads and ears carried low and their sterns drooping with fatigue. The tips of their sterns were stained with red from the vicious needles of the gorse.

'Vivid, come along,' said Tony to a weary little bitch that lagged behind.

Voices murmured and rose and fell to the hollow sound of horses jogging slowly and the soft rustle of hound feet on the road.

Below us the shapes of trees and hedges showed only dimly, but on our hilltop the light still lingered and the hedges and the grass were crisp with hoar frost that the afterglow had faintly dyed with red. It was freezing and the stars in the gathering darkness shone with brilliant hardness. The hooves of the horses struck bright sparks from an occasional flint in the road's surface.

We found the hound van waiting at the cross roads, and the pack surged round it as the two whips dropped off their horses.

Mickey waited to help the second horsemen shorten their stirrup leathers and tuck the irons up close to the saddles of the horses that they were going to lead.

The back of the hound van dropped down with a bang, making a gangway, and the hounds trotted up it. Tony picked up a shy hound from between the wheels and pushed it in with the rest.

Bill Scott and Polly McCalmont, the ends of their cigarettes glowing red in the darkness, climbed into their cars and roared away into the night as Jack Burney turned his horse's head for home.

John Toomey and the two whips pulled on their greatcoats and got into the front of the van. The engine throbbed, and as they rolled away the two grooms took a led horse on each side of the one they were riding and jogged back to the Hunt stables through Cloneen village, where the low whitewashed houses were bright with lamp-lit windows. Behind the plate-glass window of the public-house rows of bottles and polished glasses gleamed and winked through a mist of tobacco smoke.

Yearning for my stable I flung the distance behind me with the muffled beat of my slow swinging trot. Steeped in tiredness we passed rushy fields that spread away under the rising moon and little ponds set with gnarled gorse and rippled with semi-circles of the moon's reflected light.

Stars glittered above the naked shapes of the trees whose shadows lay on the road in bars, and as we climbed the ridge the lights shone out along the dim line of the mountain and the glare of a big town made the eastern heaven dun.

Mickey walked for a while with his hand on my withers while the dogs in distant farms barked uneasily.

It was late when we stepped into the shaft of lamplight that flooded from the stable door. 'What kept you so late?' demanded Connolly, standing in the gateway. 'It was a great hunt we had,' said Mickey, as he slid off my back on to the cobbles.

18

The big snow

AFTER Christmas there was a black frost. The days had a hard brightness and were bitterly cold. Icicles hung from the gutter above my stable, and drip, drip, dripped into the water butt, and every night the stars glittered brilliantly, and distant sounds travelled clearly to us through the thin air.

The fields were iron hard, and a white rime covered the grass. Birds were hungry and fought bitterly for the scraps of oats on the manure heap, or hopped sadly about the yard fluffed out until they looked like small round balls of feathers. Chaffinches came and blackbirds, and the big arrogant great tit with his bold colouring of black and yellow. He hung upside down on a twig for a moment, and then swooped sideways to chase some fragile blue tits from a scrap of bread.

In the beech trees three or four rooks sat hunched and waiting. Dan told Mickey that before such weather the flocks split up, and the rooks in twos and threes went to the trees round the cottages where they might pick up some food.

'Ay, you can always tell,' he said. 'There'll always be hard weather when you see them hanging about the houses.'

The frost held and the roads were too slippery for exercising. Small boys going to school had made a slide outside the yard gate and his father told Mickey not to take me out. 'I won't have that pony skating all over the road,' he said. 'You can leave her till the thaw comes.'

'Sure she'll be lepping out of her hide by that time,' said Mickey.

'Well, go and ask Dan what you'll do with her,' said his father, and Mickey went.

'He says to make a straw ring to ride her on,' he said, when he came back. 'With my straw! Thank you for nothing!' said Michael Connolly shortly. 'Hold on now; you can spread that manure heap across the yard if you want to and exercise on that. There's enough straw there to bed an elephant, and mind you throw it back when you're done with it, no leaving it scattered all over the place.'

Mickey got a fork and a barrow and spent the whole afternoon making a ring in the yard. When it was done it was over eight feet wide and six inches deep, and as the yard was quite large it made a good place to exercise on. But it was very boring. We rode round and round and round it, and then turned and rode the other way.

One morning when I went out I was very fresh. The air was keen and cold and I was still having the same ration of oats that I had had when I was hunting. As soon as Mickey was in the saddle I put down my head and bucked. It was a lovely feeling stretching all my muscles. The straw and stuff flew up behind my heels. Mickey stuck four bucks and then I felt him slipping, so I jumped sideways and he came over my shoulder with a bump, and landed, sitting on the manure ring.

'Lucky you made it soft, you came off very pretty!' said a voice at the gateway, and Dan walked into the yard. I was play-bucking about the place, and Mickey scrambled up, knocked the dirt off himself and catching me, scrambled back into the saddle.

'You want to keep a good hold of her head when she comes out,' said Dan. 'Don't let her get it down and then she can't buck. What oats are you giving her?'

'The same as before,' said Mickey.

'You may knock her down a couple of pounds while she's doing nothing,' said Dan. 'It only does them harm to feed them up and keep them idle, we don't want trouble with her legs, there's nothing worse for a horse than too much grub and too little work, unless it's too much work and too little grub.'

He ran his hand over my hide. 'Ay, there's a bit of humour here,' he said, feeling some spots under the skin. 'You can give her some Glauber salts in her mash tomorrow night, Mick.'

'Ah, I wish this old frost would break,' Mickey grumbled. 'I'm sick of riding round this rotten old ring.'

'Hurry up there, Mick,' shouted his father. 'I'll be wanting you to give me a hand with the cross-cut, we're nearly out of firing.'

That night the wind swung round to the east and for days an east wind blight crept across the land, a bitter haze that hung over the fields making the country look grey and depressing. On the third day it lifted and the sun came out.

Towards the east there was a veil of haze blotting out the hills, and above this veil towered pile upon pile of sculptured cloud, frothing up miles high into the air against the pale blue sky. They stretched the whole length of the horizon like a tumble of frozen breakers, and stayed there in the distance, dyed pink in the evening by the setting sun. 'Caw,' cried the three rooks to each other as they lit in the tree over the yard gate and sat there ragged and hunched. 'Croak!' they said.

The next day a leaden greyness closed in overhead. The rooks huddled in their tree, and that night the wind rose, fluttering the ivy on the house and sending wisps of straw rustling dryly across the yard.

Shut warmly in my stable I heard its gathering scream as it roared across the country in great gusts, hurling itself against my stable walls and shaking the whole building. The two cows stirred uneasily at the other side of the partition. There was a humming moan in the wind that I had never heard before and the cold was bitter. Through the little stable window the stars were blotted out by flying cloud, and presently the clouds themselves were blotted by something softer than falling leaves that whirled against the glass, lit softly, slid, and piled itself up from the bottom of the pane till there was a thick covering on the outside of the window.

In the morning a little light crept greyly in. The wind still whistled and roared across the yard. It was late for my morning feed and the cows lowed impatiently to be milked. Then I heard the scraping sound of a shovel clearing away something. It came gradually nearer the door and I heard Mickey's voice shouting to his father above the whine of the wind.

After a lot of scraping light began to come in under the door, and presently it was dragged open and Mickey came in, the wind slammed the door after him, and I could see that he was wet and his coat and cap were covered with flakes of melting snow.

He put down a large armful of hay and filled my bucket. 'That'll have to do you for a while, Speedy,' he said, and went out, pushing open the door by main force, and latching it after him. I wondered why he left the top half of my door shut. I heard them go in and milk the cows, and instead of driving them out as they usually did, they left them there for the day.

All morning the sound of digging went on in the yard and in the afternoon there was a baaing of sheep, and twenty of the ewes were driven in and penned into a corner of the cow-shed. Their fleeces were wet and steaming and the hot smell of wet sheep was rank upon the air.

All that day the wind howled on, and at night there was a crash that shook the yard, as the big elm tree over the wall fell across the wood-shed roof. I leaped to my feet in the straw, not knowing what had happened, shocked awake by the splintering roar of its falling. I noticed that the wind was coming in wild rushes with a lull between, and towards morning it grew weaker and gradually died away.

The stillness that followed was so strange after those hours of turmoil that at first it disturbed me more than the trampling of the gale. Outside the silence was intense, and through the open crack of my window I saw the brilliant flashing points of light in the sky swept free from cloud, the stars looked enormous, it was freezing hard.

Scrape, scrape went spade and shovel in the yard outside my stable. Mickey knocked the frozen latch back with a stone and threw open the top of the door, letting in a rush of cold air and a flood of bright sunlight.

He tugged and pulled for some time at the bottom half of the door before he could get it to open. I ran to the door and stuck my head out. For a moment I was dazzled by the white light of sun on snow. The whole country was buried in it. The long lines of the hedges, rounded and bowed down by the weight of it, showed brown holes and hollows in their length, where a bramble had shaken itself free from its load and sprung up again.

Everything was very still under the frosty blue sky. One side of every tree was plastered with white where the wind had driven the snow against it. The boughs cracked beneath it, and where the elm had been was a splintered stump and a broken wall. The elm was a tangle of broken branches, the great trunk, half buried in a drift, was lying across the remains of what had once been the wood-shed. Everywhere the snow had drifted with the force of the blizzard. Dazzling sculptured drifts of it were piled, curling, to the tops of the hedges, and nowhere was it less than a foot deep.

The path that Mickey and his father had dug to the paddock the day before when they brought in the ewes was filled in, and the frost had put a hard crust on the snow so that the men's boots scrunched through at each step to the softer stuff beneath.

There was no sign of life in the fields except for a few blackbirds and redwings who, fluffing their feathers out, hopped mournfully about the buried hedges.

'I never remember such a storm these last forty years,' said Mickey's father, scraping the snow off his boots on the doorstep.

All day they worked in the drifts digging out sheep up at the farm and bringing them down to the yard. The store cattle and calves were driven down to the paddock beyond the wall. They came slowly down the road floundering through the snow, their breath hanging on the air.

When they stopped in the yard a cloud of steam arose from them, hanging over them so that they stood in a fog of their own making.

'Hup! How! Hup!' shouted Mickey as he drove them through the gate, Shep snapping at their heels. Night came early with a frosty sunset, and silence fell more completely, every sound blotted out by the thick snow underfoot.

For a week we were snowbound. The main road was coated with frozen lumps of snow and ice, and Mickey and his father spoke of stock and even people lost all over the country.

'The big snow,' as it came to be called, had come with such suddenness to a country where snow was unusual that no one was prepared for it, and many farms and villages were cut off. When it melted the rivers, filled to the top with snow water, overflowed, and the land along their banks was flooded. Our river below the paddock was turned to a great brown sweeping stretch of water that flowed smoothly and sullenly between the fields, and roared beneath the bridge and down the mill weir.

Three weeks later, when we hunted again, there were drifts of snow at the side of the road, dirty and melting, and in the ditches and hollows deep snow still lingered.

Mickey spent much time foddering the stock in the paddock. While the snow lasted they were fed on straw and what hay could be spared, and they stood lowing at the yard gate till Mickey came out in the evening with great pitchfork loads of feed.

The sheep penned in the yard were fed with mangolds and hay, and they baaed to each other as they walked about in the brown sludge.

When the snow had melted to a few inches, and when he had time, Mickey took me out in the field and trotted me round and round it to prevent the snow balling in my hooves. I snorted and bounced when I was led out into it, and all the way round the field I stepped up to my chin and blew through my nose at the strangeness of it.

Scuds of snow flew up behind us as we trotted round in the keen cold air. I was delighted to get out of my stable again.

19

The run of the season

ON a cold morning in February Mickey and I were jogging slowly to the meet with two other horses that were stabled at the farm next door.

'There won't be much of a scent this morning,' Mickey said to Matt Clancy, the old groom, who was riding beside us. 'You never can tell, ' he replied. 'I've seen days when you could swear there'd be a scent and a fox would cross right under the noses of the hounds, and they could do nothing with it. I've seen them run in a snowstorm from Ballyconnel away over to the back of Martin Fennessy's, and I've seen them run in March when the ground was as hard as a board and the dust was blowing up in our faces, and there was a grand scent. And the next day there wasn't a particle. There's no accounting for it seemingly.'

The old man fell silent as we jogged down the lane, our hooves splashing up the water in the puddles. The sun shone on the blue-black tarmac and threw our shadows on the grass siding, so that they ran beside us. I watched my shadow as it slid along, distorted and ungainly against the brown hedge, with Mickey's shadow rising and falling in the saddle. No matter how fast I galloped I could never run away from it, it was always tied to my feet whenever the sun came out.

A hail shower whipped our faces as we dropped down the hill to the village, and cars came past us, slowing down as they drove up behind the led horses. Three big horse boxes and a trailer rumbled down the road, and in front of us we saw more horses going to the meet. The men riding with their collars turned up against the hail.

We trotted into the village and pulled up among the horses gathered there. Cars were drawn up on each side of the road, and the hunting people were walking about looking for their horses and talking to each other.

Mickey led me about to keep me warm, and the sun came out after the shower, striking a gleam from the wet roadway.

Pink coats showed here and there among the crowd as men took off their waterproofs. The pack stood under the trees in the little square, and as soon as the Master mounted, they moved off.

We fell in behind them, and the long line of horses clattered down the road to the covert. There was a horse on each side of me. A big black heavyweight and a keen-eared brown cob with a boy riding it. In front were the tails of three big horses, their pink-coated riders rising and falling in their saddles as we jogged along. 'Doesn't look much of a day for scent, does it?' said one man to his neighbour.

We cantered down to the covert through a wide field, and I played with my snaffle and bounced in the air with excitement, till Mickey gave me my head. We pulled up in the gateway opposite the covert and stood there in a bunch, sixty horses all eager and waiting.

The pack stood bunched beside John Toomey's horse, their heads turned to the covert. Their eyes looked from the covert to his face and back again. They whimpered and waited on tip-toe. Then he waved them in and they raced through the covert fence.

Almost at once a whip holloaed the fox away. I saw it running down the field, a big fox with a fine brush. He leaped to the top of the bank and looked back with his pad lifted. Then he dropped down with a twist of his brush and crossed the next field.

'I'll bet he's a traveller,' said the man next to me. 'That feller means to go all right,' said his neighbour. I shivered with excitement as I felt Mickey's knees grip my sides and he shortened the reins in his hand. He was leaning forward ready to go. Everyone edged up a little, pressing towards the gateway.

The leading hounds were out, the body of the pack scrambling over the fence; they were all out now and they ran down the field to the double, full cry.

'Give them time! Give them time!' said the Master. 'Let them settle down to it. If we ride on top of them now we'll spoil our own sport.'

The pack poured over the double and ran across the next field.

Christy and Tony cantered along by the covert fence as John Toomey put his horse at the big bank, landed on the top, and jumped out over the far ditch with a swish of the big bay horse's tail as he landed.

'Now you may go if you can catch them,' said Colonel Scott.

The field gathered itself into a bunch at the gate, and dissolved into sixty galloping horses, all racing for the double. We had a good start and came galloping at it.

Mickey steadied me as we came up to it. I saw the ditch, deep and brown, widen below me, then with a bound I was on the bank, changed feet, and jumped out over the sapling-tangled drain beyond it.

Mickey pushed me on till we were with the first ten horses, and the pack was a field ahead of us. They were running hard and already the field was tailed out.

Fence after fence we crossed. Once we jumped some poles in a gap and once we came to an iron bar slung across a gateway. It was tied to the posts with wire. John Toomey and most of the horses swung to the right looking for a better place in the fence. Mickey pulled up, he shortened his reins and cantered me at it, giving me my head as I took off, swinging forward with me. I tucked my legs up and sailed over, but it was a high bar and I just rapped it with my hooves as I jumped it.

We were by ourselves, the hounds were running a field ahead, and running hard. As their cry came back to me I shook my head and would have raced down the slope, but Mickey held me in. He kept me going easily along, steadying me at my fences, and later in the run I was glad that he had nursed my strength.

As we swung through a cattle gap in a fence we saw a man in front of us cutting the hedge, and just then hounds checked. Mickey pulled me up and jumped off to rest me. I stood and drew the air into my lungs, my sides heaving; it had been a fast gallop.

The moment the pack checked they spread out, casting this way and that along the headland and out into the field.

Mickey stood and watched them. 'Did you see him?' he called to the man who was cutting the hedge.

'I did not,' he shouted back.

There was a thud, thud, thud of the hooves coming up behind us, and John Toomey galloped up with what was left of the field. The pack had got their heads up now. 'Did you see them check?' he asked Mickey. 'They had the line up to the gap here,' Mickey said.

John Toomey saw the man cutting the far hedge, calling his hounds to him, and trotted back through the gap with the pack all round him. The gap and the field round it was foiled by the hooves of the horses. He made a wide cast round the field and in the corner of the fence where the gap was, hounds picked up the line.

The fox must have run to the gap, seen the man working there, and turned back on his tracks across the field, then hearing hounds coming down wind to him, he had turned off to one side and left the field at the corner of the fence.

'Forrard! Forrard! Forrard!' John Toomey cried, as the pack raced forward again. At the end of the next field the fox had turned left-handed, and once more he ran down wind. I had got my second wind now and if Mick had not held me in I should have raced on at the top of my speed. We crossed a low hill and saw hounds running hard along a line of trees to a big ditch at the bottom of the field.

John Toomey, Christy, and Tony were going hard down the hill and we galloped at it in line; it was a wide black ditch with golden reeds growing up through the water at the bottom and feathering above its ragged mouth.

All together we came at it, hooves thundering, side by side. The three pink coats leaned forward, Tony long and lean, and John Toomey and Christy, little jockeys of men. The ditch widened as we came to it, four pairs of heels drove into the sides of four horses and they lifted into the air, flew through the air over the ditch, over the water and feathery reeds out into the next field, landing sound and galloping on. That was what it felt like to jump a big place, going fast.

We crossed a road jumping at a slant on to the grass siding, so that we should not land on the tarmac which would have meant a certain fall.

We ran through a farmyard where our hooves clattered on the cobbles and chickens fled squawking in front of us. We galloped over long grass fields, and trotted up the drainage furrows of a plough land.

We gave John Toomey a lead over an awkward fence that his horse refused. I did not feel a stake that ripped the skin from my fetlock, I was so excited, so keen to be with hounds. But as we came up a long slope crowned with trees I began to feel my breath coming shorter and my heart bumping between my ribs. The blue distance widened below us as we topped the rise, and the horses galloping beside me were beginning to tire though their riders had eased them up the slope. There were only a few of us left now and we had come a long way.

Then the cry of the pack took on a deeper note. They dashed down the headland fierce for blood. 'They're close to him now,' said John Toomey. Every horse took hold of his bit and raced forward answering the excitement of their riders.

At the end of the field there was a deep drop into a muddy ditch where a drinking-place had been made for cattle. There was no other way out of the field and John Toomey put his horse at it. The old hunter dropped down into it with a splash, tripped over something under the mud, and rolled over, across John Toomey. They scrambled out smothered in mud, and John Toomey pulled the horse out by the bridle.

Mickey put me at it and I jumped from the top into the slough. I felt my forefeet go down, stumbled, rolled over, and as I fell two horses came in on each side of me. Three of us rolled and wallowed there together. Dripping with mud and water Mickey got clear, and I scrambled out after him. There was an open sewer under the mud.

Mickey flung himself into the saddle and we tore down the field. At the end of it a whirlpool of hounds surged and swayed and tussled with a full-throated snarl.

John Toomey leaped off his horse and beat them back. At his feet lay the dead fox with the hounds baying all round it. Christy galloped up, threw Mickey his reins and leaped off his horse. 'Whoo, Whoop!' he cried with his hand to his ear. 'Whoo, Whoop!'

The horses stood steaming, their sides heaving. 'He was a good fox,' a man said, wiping the mud out of his eye. There was mud all over Mickey, in his red hair, on his fox-head tie, and the top half of his old Sunday suit that he wore over an ancient pair of breeches that Dan had given him.

John Toomey stood in the middle of the pack holding

the dead fox above his head, round him they leaped and bayed. High in the air the brown body flew, and the pack closed over it as it fell. 'Whoo, Whoop!' my blood leaped with excitement. John Toomey's horse whickered.

Colonel Scott walked over to John Toomey and spoke to him. He nodded and came towards us. 'Here young feller,' he said. 'Stick that in your pocket.' He handed Mickey the brush.

20

Preparation

THE smell of spring was in the air, sap rising, growth pushing upwards. Rocking on a high wind, rooks swayed above
the beech trees trying to tack near enough to catch the
topmost twig with their claws, their beaks clamped firmly
on the twigs that they carried for their nests.

Cloud shadows swept over the short bitten grass of the
wide fields, dappling the sunlight. At the other side of the
river a man was ploughing with two brown horses.

From my stable I could see the horses' heads tossing up
and down as they drew the ploughshare through the soil,
and up the wet blue-black line of the newly turned furrow
rooks and seagulls rose and fell, fighting almost under the
horses' feet for grubs and beetles.

I had not been for my usual morning exercises and was
feeling restive. With every ounce of superfluous fat turned
into hard muscle by steady walking and slow trotting, I
was fit to jump out of my skin.

It was more than three weeks since I had had a hunt, and
yesterday I had seen the Harriers jogging up the road, and
shivered with excitement.

Instead, however, of hacking to the meet we had been
out early, walking and jogging up a long hilly road that
ran past Dan's yard, and when I came in I had been
watered and given a feed of oats, groomed and wisped and
rugged up as usual. I was having more oats now than I had
been having while I was hunting and was fed five times a
day instead of three, under old Dan's directions.

Early each morning Mickey gave me a little water and a
feed of oats, and as soon as the cows were milked he rode

me out, walking and trotting slowly up the hilly road and back by Dan's yard. We turned in there and the old man came out and looked at me, and felt my skin, and ran his hand over my muscles.

On each side of his yard, heads looked out over the half-doors of loose boxes: shy eyes and unclipped faces of young horses. The two greyhounds came bounding across the cobbles.

When we got home Mickey would water me and give me a feed of oats, and groom and wisp my hide before he rugged me up. After that I would have some of my hay, and in the afternoon when the sun was just over the tree tops I would have more oats and a drink, and in the evening after the cows were milked I was given water, another feed, and the bulk of my hay. Then Mickey would take off my sheet and brush me over with the body-brush for a few minutes and then wisp my body with steady strokes.

Wisping played a very important part in my conditioning and preparation, for careful feeding, work, and wisping in the right proportions were necessary to bring my body to that pitch of fitness and condition that would enable all its parts to stand the strain of a hard race without breaking down.

Each time the wisp fell I braced my muscles to meet it, relaxing after the stroke so that my muscles developed and my skin was massaged and sleek.

The setting sun streamed into my box, shining on the straw, and distant sounds of dogs driving cattle and young lambs calling to the ewes drifted in from the quiet fields as he wisped. 'There now,' Mickey would say, running his hand down my neck and putting on my rug and sheet, he would look to see that the breast strap was tight enough and that the surcingle was not twisted. A bucket would chink in the yard as he went out and shut the door.

Late in the evening I was given a final feed of oats before I went to sleep.

This had been my regular routine for nearly three weeks, and when presently Mickey came to my stable with a saddle and bridle, I was longing to go out and walk through the lanes in the sunlight.

The yard rang with the clang of iron on stone as I curt-seyed and danced out of the gate. Children ran shouting down the road on their way to school and the rooks cawed in the bright air. Mickey held the reins in one hand and patted and stroked my arching neck with the other. I would have bucked as a car swung past us if I had not sighted a horse standing at the cross-roads with a familiar figure in the saddle. It was Dan on a young brown horse, clipped trace high.

'I was just coming in when I saw you, Mick,' he said, as we walked side by side down the green grass lane to the yard. 'We'll give her a gallop today up the hill of Cloneen. I have old Roscannon here, getting him ready for the Clo-neen Cup, and it'll do no harm to open his pipes a bit.'

'Should we not give her more galloping, Dan?' said Mickey.

'She'll have plenty of galloping before she's done,' said Dan. 'Don't you worry.'

'There's only one thing that I wish, Dan,' said Mickey. 'I wish I had the riding of her myself.'

'Well, now, I wish you had, Mick, but what'd be the good of you riding her when you never rode a race before? It's not as if it was for the fun of the thing. If we can get a price on her we'll make a good thing out of this, if we can pull it off; we're lucky to get Mrs Jackson to ride her.

'Riding,' he went on, 'isn't the same thing as hareing across the country after the hounds; you want to know all the ins and outs of it. I remember . . .' As they talked we turned in at the gate of the yard.

Dan's yard was a square old mud-walled farmyard. Three sides of it were occupied by loose boxes with wooden partitions and cobbled floors. Above them were derelict hay lofts where pigeons strutted and cooed. At the end of the yard stood a narrow two-storeyed house, one room thick, with the roughcast flaking off it and showing the stone underneath. Pigeons sat on the slate roof and the green door stood ajar with a moth-eaten black cat sleeping on the worn step.

House and yard had once been whitewashed and the wooden half-doors of the loose boxes painted red, but now the paint was peeling and long green marks ran down the walls from the gutters.

A pump stood in the middle of the yard with a stone trough below it. 'Gub-ooka-tagoo,' cried the pigeons, strutting around it on quick pink feet. As we walked through the gate a flight of them rose and circled overhead, the sun catching the white underside of their wings in a gleaming flash as they wheeled sideways.

Nine interested faces turned towards us over the loose-box doors, bay, brown, and grey, and among them a keen clipped head with a silky mane and forelock that looked in a different class to the young unclipped faces round it.

'That's Roscannon over there in the end box,' said Dan, with a jerk of his head towards it. 'He's the boy that can gallop.'

'How old is he now, Dan?' said Mickey. 'Coming on ten, and if his legs were as good as the rest of him he wouldn't be here. That horse was bred to jump Aintree, but there's a good many point-to-point's in the old lad yet if we can keep him sound.'

'How'll you do that, Dan?' said Mickey.

'That's the way,' said Dan, and Mickey said no more, he knew, as Dan would say, that 'Curiosity killed the cat.'

'Hold her there now till I put in this feller,' the old man

said, and he led his horse towards one of the boxes. I lipped at the grass that grew between the cobbles of the yard while Mickey stood with my rein slipped over his arm, and the pigeons crooned to each other, strutting in the sunlight.

'Peter,' called Dan, and a little man with bandy legs and an old polo-necked sweater came round the corner with a bucket and grinned at Mickey.

'How's the race horse?' he said.

'OK,' said Mickey.

Peter helped Dan with the horses. I had often seen him out hunting, coaxing a green youngster along, never fussing it or knocking it about, but when the time came, getting it into a good hunt, and letting it go along in front. He never overfaced a horse, knew exactly what he wanted to do, and rode with a quiet determination that gave all his horses complete confidence in him.

'Don't be getting so excited,' he would say to Mickey. 'Sure I can't help it,' Mickey would say. 'I make up my mind before I go hunting that I won't get excited and then I see the hounds and I go clean off my head, and Speedy's the same.'

'So she would be,' Peter would say. 'Whatever you are your horse will be much the same; if you hesitate over your fences and don't know what you want to do, your horse will take to refusing, same as if you overfaced him, or jab him in the mouth. A lazy man will make a lazy horse, and a nervous man a nervous horse nine times out of ten. Of course there are old stagers that don't care what sort of a man there is on their back so long as they can get to hounds, but even they will spoil in time with a bad jock up. I'm talking of young horses. It's the training they get when they're young that makes them or ruins them, they're like kids, you want to have a lot of patience with them.'

'Did you ever get a bad fall, Peter?' Mickey had asked him once.

'Ay I did, many's the time,' he said. 'There was one time that I was schooling a horse and he caught me a clip over the ear when he fell. I was eight days unconscious that time. I felt a bit nervous after I started again, but I couldn't do without the horses. You'd be terribly lonely without them.

'I never hurt myself yet,' said Mickey.

'Well, you never go so well or get the same enjoyment out of it as you do when you're young, on a good pony, before you know what fear is; it's the best time in your life.'

'I always think,' said Mickey, 'that there'll never be anything to beat riding Speedy at the top of a good hunt, going over the fences with the hounds the length of a field away. There's nothing in the world to beat it.'

'Ay, I used to think that, too,' said Peter. 'Them were the days.'

Listening to them, I felt that what they said was true. We know from the feel of the rider's hand on the rein and the grip of his knees on the saddle a great deal of what goes on in his mind. I knew when Mickey saw something on the side of the road that he thought I would shy at, for I would feel his knees tighten and his hands shorten the rein, and then I would look about me to see what he was frightened of and shy because he had prepared me to.

'Leave her alone,' Dan used to tell him. 'Don't go climbing up the reins,' or, 'don't turn her head towards it, turn her head away to keep her straight.'

I knew whether Mickey was frightened, or excited, or at ease, and I responded to his mood.

Presently Dan came across the yard leading Roscannon, while Peter attended to the young horse that he had brought in.

'We'll go across the fields,' said Dan.

Roscannon was a great blood horse. 16.2 hands high. He was beautifully made and the muscles bulged and rippled on his shoulders and quarters and along his neck. His keen ears and big clear eye showed his health and fitness.

We rode slowly down the field where the lambs were running races along the headland and a flock of green plover rose flapping into the sunlight. 'Why was Roscannon no good for chasing?' asked Mickey.

'The legs wouldn't stand it,' said Dan; 'but he's won more point-to-points than any horse in this part of the country. When he comes out for the Farmers' Race the other horses might as well go home.'

The wind lifted our manes gently and we jumped out over an open ditch in the corner of the field and pulled up to a walk again.

'We'll give her a schooling gallop next week,' said Dan. 'She's used to taking her fences fast, so she won't want much sharpening up. She jumps off all right,' he added.

Mickey had taught me to jump off the moment the field moved forward so that we should be in our stride while the other horses were only getting their balance, and many a good start we got when hounds left covert.

Through the gap we walked and found ourselves at the bottom of a long field near Cloneen. This field sloped gently uphill for half a mile, to a tall beechwood with laurel covert beneath the trees. It was a lively sight when hounds came to draw here during the season, and the field jogged up the hill behind the pack; and a better one when from the top you saw the hunt streaming away across the fields after the fox had found the six counties lay spread out below you, wood, and field and hill and hollow, till all design was lost in misty blueness that merged with the horizon.

'We'll give them a long half-pace gallop,' said Dan. 'You

keep even with me and hold her together.' We started with
our backs to the fence and jumped off, Dan and Mickey
leaning forward on our withers. Roscannon galloped like
clockwork. I soon fell into his stride and we galloped steadily side by side towards the covert on the top of the hill.
The grass seemed to flow towards us and vanish beneath
our thudding hooves. Nearer and nearer came the
beechwood, and the sun shone on the laurel leaves as we
passed it and galloped along the top of the ridge, below
which the fields fell away on either side, and our manes
were lifted by the wind that cooled our faces.

Slowly Dan pulled up to a trot and then to a walk,
Mickey keeping pace with him. Roscannon blew through
his nose to clear his wind. So did I. I was blowing a bit after
the climb, but neither of us was distressed.

'It's not the distance so much as the pace that tires a
horse,' said Dan. We walked steadily back through the
fields to the yard. 'Give her a couple of hours' walking and
trotting every day,' he went on, 'and bring her over here on
Wednesday and we'll give her another gallop. Two will be
enough for this week.'

My preparation took a month to complete, and for the
last fortnight I had two fast gallops a week in a field near
Dan's house and one long half-pace gallop up Cloneen
Hill.

Mickey gave much of his time to wisping and grooming,
feeding and exercising, and was let off much of his other
work. Often his father would walk across the yard and
look at me with his head on one side, questioning Mickey
about my work. He took a great interest in me now, and I
think he was proud of the way that Mickey had gone out
hunting, for he seldom grumbled at the time the boy spent
in my stable as he would have done a while ago.

Exercising in the sunny spring weather we rode down
the lanes where cushions of primroses studded the banks.

Willow catkins were out and the yellow tassels on the hazel twigs. And against the brown of a line of beech trees was a green mist of unfolding leaves where a chestnut was coming out, or a cherry tree, white with blossom leaned over the ditch.

Hares sat up in the fields to watch us pass. The Harriers had ended their season at the beginning of March and the coursing season was over, so for some months they would lead a protected life, guarded by law against greyhound, hound, and gun.

One morning a fox trotted lazily across the road in front of us with his ears pricked forward and his brush down. He turned round to look at us and dropped down through the fence into the next field, where he stopped and had another look. Mickey pulled me up and watched him as he trotted across the grass in the sunlight and sat down on a bank to scratch himself. We trotted slowly on watching him as he nosed along the line of the hedge until he disappeared behind a bramble tangle.

I loved those sunny mornings when the wind ruffled the shining ivy on the tall elm trees and swayed the drifts of daffodils under the twisted branches by square old houses.

There was a feeling that I always had when we topped the rise beyond Dan's house: 'It's good to be alive,' and my hooves on the road repeated it – 'It's good to be alive.'

One morning Connolly came out with a sheet of paper in his hand. 'I can't make head or tail of this,' he said. 'It's the entry form. You'd better take it across to Dan and get him to fill it up, and you've got to get your certificate from Colonel Scott. You could ride over there tomorrow.

'This one's been hunted fairly anyway,' said Mickey, scratching my withers.

The next time I went to Dan's house there was a car in

the yard. It was a low green car with a long bonnet, and near it a girl with a camel-hair coat over her jodhpurs and a polo-necked sweater was talking to Dan. She turned to look at me as we walked into the yard, her grey eyes widening in her small, high-cheek-boned face.

She said good morning to Mickey, who touched his cap, and she patted me behind the ear. 'How high does she stand?' she said to Dan.

'Just fifteen hands,' said Dan.

'A bit small for the Light Weight isn't she?' the girl wondered.

'As small as she is you'd be surprised at the way she can go,' said Dan.

'Is this the mare that finished the good hunt from Clonaney?' she asked, remembering.

'She is, Mrs Jackson,' said Mickey.

'Ah, I've heard of her,' said the girl and landed lightly in the saddle. I felt at once from the way she sat and from her light touch on the rein that she knew exactly what she was doing and how to do it. Here was one who rode as Terry rode, and as she collected me between feel of snaffle and pressure of leg, my old training came back to me and we moved as one.

The schooling fences lay across a mile of country at the other side of the road and we cantered gently down to them, old Roscannon snorting through his nose. I played with my snaffle, giving to the give and take of pressure on the bit. 'She moves nicely,' said the girl.

This time when we jumped off, we galloped to a gap in the fence where the hedge had been cut away. There was an open ditch and at a sharp nudge of legs against my sides, I took off and flew over beside Roscannon. Side by side we galloped down to the next fence, our hooves beating a galloping rhythm as the grass slid beneath us.

Together we came to the small double, took off, rose,

touched the top with our hooves and landed out over the ditch into the next field. I leaned against my bit and tried to race ahead, but my rider held me level with Roscannon's brown nose and we sailed out over an open ditch, galloped across another field and chased a flying cloud shadow across the ditch at the end of it.

Slowly we pulled up to a standstill. 'She hardly needs another gallop,' said the girl. 'Better knock her off and have her on her toes on the day of the race,' agreed Dan. 'The galloping she's doing will be enough for her.'

If the rain held off the going would be good, they decided.

There were still ten days to dry up the country before the Point-to-Point. 'I'll have her there before the Open Race,' said Dan. 'Are you riding in it this year, Ma'am?'

'I am,' said the girl. 'I'll be riding the Widgeon, and Pride of Knockree in the Maiden. There's some hot stuff up against us in the Light Weights I'm afraid.'

'Well there's many a slip,' said Dan.

21

The point-to-point

THE morning was bright and the soft April wind blew white puffs of cloud across the sky. Mickey took me out early and gave me a short gallop in Dan's field. When we came back to the stable, the big bell of the Chapel was booming half past nine.

'Here's your rug, Mick,' said Dan, coming across to my stable where Mickey was wisping me. I lifted my head from the bucket where I had been lipping round to feel if there were any grains of oats left from my feed and saw that he carried a small dark blue rug over his arm. It was bound with red braid.

'I'll give you the loan of this for the occasion,' he said.

Over his other arm he carried a small saddle, a light snaffle bridle, a circingle, and a weight cloth. 'We'll want a circingle as well as a girth today,' he said, opening the stable door.

'The race is at 3.30, so you'll want to get there before the Cup. Lead her round before you have to go into the saddling ring, don't keep her standing in the cold wind. Go off and make yourself respectable now, you're not going into the ring with your trousers tied round the legs with a bit of string.'

Mickey went off with a grin, and came back later with his red hair well watered down and his fox-head tie and dark blue Sunday suit. He slipped the bridle over my head, put on the blue sheet that Dan had given him and led me out of the stable and down the street.

As we picked our way along the narrow lane that led to the course a distant roar of voices drifted across the fields, rose to a clamour of cheering, and then ceased. The wind carried with it a smell of crushed grass, trampled into mud, and the heavily sweet smell of the yellow gorse that was out all along the high ridge that overlooked the course.

I pricked my ears at the noise and sniffed the unfamiliar smells. There was a tang of smoke and of sweating horses, the taint of people and the new and bitter smell of orange peel.

At the end of the lane we turned into a field below the ridge. Into it were packed row upon row of motor cars in gleaming ranks and at the far end stood three white tents, their canvas bellying in the wind. From the gorse covered hill above us a black mass of people swarmed down to join the crowd that swayed round the bookies' stands and the side shows and the drink tent.

Here and there horses were being led up and down, they were heavily rugged, yet some of them shivered with excitement and the keen air. Steaming horses that had just been unsaddled were being rubbed over, their sides were heaving and their nostrils, distending and contracting, showed the red membrane inside.

Everywhere people were coming and going. Countrymen in their Sunday clothes or heavy overcoats green with age, women in tweeds with shooting sticks and men in riding breeches and soft hats. Among them moved tinkers with wild hair and dark eyes in brown faces.

They stood in little circles round the horses that they were interested in, or crowded round the saddling ring and by the bookies' stands.

Girls with white aprons and black shawls carried great baskets of fruit, or bundles of race cards. 'Four pence each th'apples, oranges, and bananas,' they cried. 'Four pence each the ripe bananas,' or 'race card, card of the races, racing card'. 'Even money on the field,' shouted the bookies.

Everything was new and exciting and bewildering. I walked a-tiptoe with my head up and ears pricked looking from side to side. Mickey bought a race card and led me up and down, talking to the friends who stopped to have a word with him. Presently Dan came up with Connolly behind him.

'The course is in great order,' he said. 'Couldn't be better.'

'What won the Maiden?' said Mickey.

'The Swallow,' said Dan. 'I got fives on her. Young Mr Scott won the hunt race on the roan. Himself and Jack Burney came up the straight together, there wasn't a head between them, and I don't know which of the two would have won if the roan hadn't leaped off the ground at the very post and got her nose in front. It was a great race, and plenty of spills in it. Three of them came down together at the first fence.'

'I don't like that sharp turn at all,' said Connolly. 'The crowd comes pressing in and it baulks a horse.'

'Ah,' said Dan. 'Are you going to have a bet?' he asked Mickey. 'With old Roscannon running I wouldn't fancy anything else.'

'What about the horse Mrs Jackson is riding?' said Mickey. 'Ah she's a chancy old beggar,' said Dan. 'I wouldn't fancy her at all. Go an' have a bet on Roscannon and I'll hold the mare.' He took my reins and Mickey vanished into the crowd. Presently he shoved his way back. 'Even money,' he said. 'Bad luck to it,' said Dan and went off to see to his horse.

In one corner of the field was a roped-in enclosure, already people were gathering round it and a horse was being led slowly round inside the ring.

He had a sheet over him, dark blue with red braid, his legs were bandaged and his mane was plaited and braided. He was a big horse and carried his head proudly with his ears pricked forward. He stepped out delicately with springy tread on the crushed grass.

Gazing round him at the crowd, he looked proud and aloof, as if he had a right to be there and it was well that they should look at him. On his neck the muscles swelled and little veins stood out under the skin. Muscles rippled beneath his sheet, on his forearms and quarters, and he arched his neck to the hand that held the reins. The next time they came round the ring I saw that it was Roscannon and that Peter was leading him.

'Ah, he's a grand horse,' I heard someone say.

Another horse came into the ring, a grey chunky little horse that danced and sidled and snatched at the hand of the man who led him. He had a hogged mane and his tail was braided into a tight knot. Racing boots were on his legs, with cotton wool showing over the top and bits of foam flecked his sheet when he tossed his head.

Behind him followed a little brown mare who walked with her head down, taking no notice of anyone.

A big black horse with a white blaze in a wild eye danced into the ring followed by a lean greyhound of a bay that looked as hard as wire.

'Hi! Hi!' rose a warning shout by the gateway and the crowd scattered, as a nervous, sweating chestnut bounded through, pulling the boy who led her almost off his feet. She danced and sidled and then lashed out, so that other horses gave her plenty of room.

Owners and their friends walked into the ring and stood in the centre. I saw Jack Burney and Colonel Scott and two or three others that I had noticed out hunting.

The riders came in in their colours. Mrs Jackson and Bill Scott talking to each other, a tall man with a limp, a boy hardly out of his 'teens and looking very solemn; a little old man with a lined face and legs bowed with much

riding and a young farmer who was one of the best am-
ateurs in the country.

The bookies were clamouring above the crowd. The
horses were being stripped. The chestnut got the red braid
cord of her sheet caught under her tail and started kicking
wildly until her groom deftly removed it.

'Get up, Jockeys! Get up!' called a voice in the ring. The
horses were saddled, the colours fluttered in the wind.

A groom held each horse's head as the riders were given
a leg up; suddenly their colours were silhouetted against
the sky, lifted above the heads of the crowd on to the
backs of their dancing horses.

From Roscannon's great back Bill Scott was adjusting his
stirrup leathers. His quartered cap was blue and gold, his
silk jacket blue with gold bars.

The head of Mrs Jackson's plunging grey rose and fell
between the lines of people; the horse rocked up and down
like a ship on a rough sea, as it played about, shaking the
man who led it as if he were an empty sack.

Once clear of the ring the grooms fell back and the
horses cantered down the fields to the starting-post.

As Roscannon cantered past me, his great muscles driving his body along like oiled clockwork, his ears cocked
forward, he looked sure of himself and unhurried. Bill
Scott was leaning forward in the saddle, patting his neck.
'There goes the winner,' said a voice from the crowd.

Already the gorse-covered ridge was black with people.
Out in the country a lonely flutter of red and white
showed where flags marked the fences. They showed
against the green grass away to the left over the fields and I
saw them again up a low rise to the sky-line. They were
lost behind a farmhouse and wood at the top of the hill. On
the right they marked a line of fences coming down hill
into a ploughed field and beyond the plough they fluttered
on the top of a big double with a line of Scotch fir trees

along it. The trunks of the fir trees were dyed red in the sun and stood out against the grass of the fields.

In a gap in the trees a black cluster of people stood on either side of this fence, like black crows, waiting.

The flags fluttered at two open ditches in the fields under the ridge and beyond the last of these was the run-in. It was roped on each side to keep back the crowd and at the end of it red flags marked the winning-post, beside a farm cart that did duty as a judge's stand.

The end of the run-in was also the starting-post, for the course was a wide circle over about three and a half miles of country.

Tony and Christy in their pink coats came cantering up the field on two of the hunt horses. They went down to the start to clear the course, making a green lane through the crowd, and then galloped up to the first fence to keep back the people who swarmed round it.

Mickey held my reins now and from where we stood we could see the horses lining up for the start.

I could see the shifting colours against the brown line of the fence as the horses sidled and danced, fell into line and broke again. The starter's fat cob stood like a rock.

From the start to the first fence stretched a black wall of people on each side of a green lane. Every face was turned one way, there was a dead silence. Suddenly an 'Ah' rose from the crowd. Five horses leaped forward and swept down towards us, their hooves thundering.

They came at the first fence as if it wasn't there, the open ditch had a sharp turn to the right and the horses were bunched close together. Swish they sailed through the air, but the little brown mare was blinded by the horses in front of her and failed to take off properly. She dropped her hind legs in the ditch and rolled over and over as the chestnut, coming behind her, cleared the ditch, fallen horse, and crouching rider in one enormous bound.

Then the crowd closed in and half-way down the field the leading horse was swinging left-handed to take the next fence.

A flying cloud shadow chased them as they went and the sun lit the shower of water that their hooves flung high in the flooded bottom, breaking it into a million diamonds.

Again they rose in the air, sailing out over the ditch; they were more spread out now and the grey was in the lead, and old Roscannon, shaking at his bit, was creeping up on him stride by stride.

Where the course lay uphill, towards the farmhouse on the sky-line, the colours faded and became indefinite dots bobbing up the green field.

The crowd were silent, watching. A man, his silk jacket covered in mud, walked back from the first fence with a saddle and bridle over his arm. The little mare was out of it now for good and all. 'Pity,' said the man nearest to Mickey. 'She was a good little mare.'

Up on the sky-line the specks were bobbing again, tiny effigies of horses with thin spidery legs, their riders crouched forward over their withers. The grey was still in the lead, then came three horses in a bunch and last of all the chestnut, dropping farther and farther behind. They passed out of sight over the top of the hill behind the farm house and the line of trees.

Tension dropped for a moment. A babel of chatter broke from the waiting crowd, everyone made for the run-in and a black sea of people flowed across the field and lined up against the ropes.

The judge and his party were standing on the farm wagon by the winning-post. 'I see them Dan,' shouted Mickey. 'Over beyond by the trees.' They were racing now. Coming downhill as if devils were after them. A black horse was leading, with the grey close behind him and Roscannon going steadily and apparently without effort was lying third. The line of Scotch fir trees on the top of the double hid them as they crossed the plough.

Now they were coming down the grass towards the fence. The two flags fluttered, the crowd drew back to one side. I have never seen anything like the way Roscannon jumped that fence. He took off out in the field, sailed to the top, seemed just to touch it with his hooves so quickly did he change feet, and was out over the big ditch and on down the field while the black horse was still getting into his stride on the landing side.

The crowd roared its approval. 'Come on Roscannon! Roscannon! Roscannon!' Bill Scott dropped his hands, he didn't have to hurry. They took the next fence in their stride and leading by half a field swept over the last fence and galloped up the run-in.

The crowd were cheering themselves hoarse. It was a race now between the grey and the black for second place. Neck and neck they came down the field to the last fence. I do not know what happened, but they seemed to collide in mid-air. There was a gasp from the crowd, a tangle of kicking legs on the ground and the two horses scrambled up and galloped riderless up the run-in, their loose reins and stirrups irons flapping as they charged through the crowd.

The man in the black horse's colours got up and bent over the rider who lay where she had fallen, straight out and motionless, her face flat against the muddy ground, flattened and still in her crumpled colours.

Everywhere people were running. The two whips galloped down on their horses. 'My God! what'll we do now?' said Mickey and Dan together.

They held an anxious conference, Dan and Connolly and Mickey, all talking in low voices. Mickey was urging something. Dan was doubtful and Connolly shaking his head vehemently. Presently Dan slipped away into the crowd. He came back in a minute or two with a long face.

'It's no go,' he said, 'Mrs Jackson's knocked out and I can't get anyone else to ride the mare and what's more we've got the money on. I don't know what to do.'

'Ah! let me ride her, Dan,' said Mickey. 'Haven't I been hunting her all the season and isn't it the only thing to do when we can't get a rider for her? Sure you wouldn't send her home and the race just starting?'

'Well,' said Dan, 'it's as good as lost either way, so you might as well take a chance, you can do the weight.'

He turned to Connolly and they talked together for some seconds. Connolly was obviously unwilling but he gave in at last and Mickey was in seventh heaven. 'Come on now, and we'll fix this up and get you weighed,' said Dan, and they went off towards the tents.

Michael Connolly took my reins and led me towards the saddling ring where people were already gathering round the ropes to watch the horses that were going to run.

22

The race

ALL round the paddock was a trampled sea of mud that flowed round the bookies' stand, mingled with crushed grass and betting tickets.

The bookies were shouting themselves hoarse, shouting the odds and taking bets. The sun, lower now in the west, turned the gorse on the ridge to molten gold.

'Mind out now,' warned Connolly, as he led me through the crowd and into the ring behind another horse whose tail was braided and knotted between muscular quarters.

I threw up my head and snorted as he walked round. I was hemmed in by a circle of shifting faces and watching eyes. Over the heads of the crowd the bookies' umbrellas on their boards stood up like islands.

I looked about me at the other horses. There was Shannon Girl, neat and small, with a keen little head and alert ears. She tripped along daintily in the pride of her blood, rubbing her muzzle against her attendant's arm.

Sea Mist, lean and grey, with ears laid back and tail tucked into dappled quarters.

Knight of Athmore, a dark-bay horse with a white blaze, plaited mane, and bandages on his legs.

A horse was coming into the ring. It was The Beagle, a three-quarter-bred roan, whose looks belied his turn of speed. He was a gaunt red roan with a Roman nose, ugly and powerful, and once he got going there was no holding him. He had a mean eye that was sunk deep in his head and he looked as hard as nails.

Marcus, Polly McCalmont's good-looking blood chestnut was a picture. Since I had seen him out hunting he had been kept for the point-to-points and looked in perfect condition. He tossed his head with its white blaze, and his four white-stockinged legs danced with impatience.

As they walked round the paddock I saw a black four-year-old with unplaited mane, showing the white of a wild scared eye, his neck in a lather.

The last three entries were poor-looking stuff. A chestnut weed, herring gutted, run up till he looked as if his greyhound middle would hardly bear the weight of his rider. A quiet brown horse with a sleepy eye and lop ears, and a sour-looking bay mare, over-trained and sulky, with a leg ready to lash out at the horse behind her.

Most of the horses looked keen and eager for the race, knowing the game and liking it. One or two were indifferent, and the bay mare apprehensive. She had had a hard race too many, and was sick of point-to-points.

The riders and their friends walked into the paddock and stood with the horses walking round them, talking to their owners and trainers. They shivered in the keen air that fluttered their silk shirts and tapped their black boots with their riding-whips.

Bill Scott was there, and Polly McCalmont riding side-saddle without a skirt. One or two good amateur riders whom I had seen out hunting. Standing by the gate was a well-known point-to-point rider who had come up from the south to ride Shannon Girl. And last of all came Mickey, looking very solemn in the colours that Connolly had had made for the occasion and that Mrs Jackson should have worn. They were tucked into the top of his Sunday trousers, and he carried Dan's ashplant instead of a whip.

Dan came over to Connolly. 'It's all right, Mike,' he said. 'We got permission to change the rider, and he weighed-in all right. He won't have to carry as much lead as Mrs Jackson,' which will be less deadweight.'

'Do you think we have a chance, Dan?' said Connolly.

'There seems to be very good stuff against us, and I wouldn't say we had,' said Dan; 'but we'll hope for the best. It's all we can do.'

'Get up now, Jockeys!' shouted a voice. And Dan led me into the middle of the ring. He stripped off my sheet and adjusted the saddle and weight cloth.

Horses were dancing and fidgeting round me. Bill Scott was up on Knight of Athmore. Sea Mist was kicking and plunging. Polly McCalmont, riding side-saddle, was soothing Marcus, who was getting excited and throwing his head about.

'Come on now, Mickey,' said Dan. 'Up with you.' He gave him a leg up, and I felt him land in the saddle and adjust the stirrups.

Filled with excitement, I danced with impatience to be off, trying to snatch the reins from Dan's hand.

The other horses were filing out.

'Remember now,' said Dan quietly to Mickey, 'go on as long as you feel her going well under you, and if she starts to fail before the plough take her quietly in. If she is going well and you come in front coming home, for any sake ride straight and don't go dodging about coming up to a fence, and don't look back, or you'll unbalance her. That's all now, and good luck to you. Hold her together.'

'More power, Mick,' said his father. 'Safe home.'

We made our way through the crowd that was moving towards the start. Already the ridge was dotted with people watching us as we went down the field.

Dan took his hand off my bridle, and Mickey stood up in his stirrups as we cantered down to join the other starters, who were pulling up at the end of the run-in, which was also the starting-post.

With a rattle of hooves the starter galloped up behind us. He was a stout little man with a pot hat on top of a round bearded face, and his butty roan cob was pulling his arms out.

Tony and Christy were cracking their whips to clear the course. 'Good man, Mick,' said Tony, with a grin, as we came past him.

Ten horses lined up to face the starter. I was next the outside horse, between Sea Mist and The Beagle. As we edged into line The Beagle put back his ears at me and his pig eye showed white. I laid back my ears and would have snapped at him, but at that moment Sea Mist bumped into my quarters, and I bounded to one side.

When we were nearly level the black swung round plunging, and knocked us out of line again.

Ten horses' profiles, ears cocked and eager, were tossing and playing with their snaffles for a moment.

For a moment ten faces under silk quartered caps were leaning forward. Then the flag fluttered, it fell, and with a roar of hooves we swept down the course, racing between the black lines of people towards the first fence.

One, two, three! Mickey's legs nudged my sides as we came up to the take-off, and at the third nudge I rose in the air, and with a sudden silence of hoof-beats the other horses rose with me. With a rush through the air we swept over the brown ditch and landed with a rattle of hooves on the far side.

I caught a glimpse of Tony's pink coat as he sat on his horse keeping the crowd back from the fence; then the green field lay before us, and all round me horses were galloping, their hooves beating a steady tattoo on the short-bitten grass.

Again and again I tried to pull the reins through Mickey's fingers, but he held me together and I could not go faster. I was wild with excitement, feeling nothing but the heady exhilaration that racing brings to a horse's brain, whipped to frenzy by the sound of hooves and the feel of

the wind on my face and by the rushing through the air of
my body, held back from its utmost speed by the pressure
of the bit, which drew my nose up and in and held me into
a bunch of working muscles.

Under my nose my hooves shot backwards and forwards like pistons.

With every breath I drew the cold air rushed into my
lungs, and once or twice I snorted through my nose to
clear it.

The black horse and The Beagle were galloping on each
side of me, hard held, their great muscles working under
their skin, flecks of foam flying back from their bits. The
shoes of the horses in front of us flashed bright in the sunlight.

At times, beyond Marcus's chestnut quarters and his
braided tail, I could see the chestnut weed that was making
the running. Behind him Knight of Athmore was going
easily, with Sea Mist at his stirrup; and at Sea Mist's quarters was the sulky mare, with Shannon Girl beside her.
Behind us the big brown horse with the lop ears was dropping back, and I could hear his loud breathing fading farther away.

As we splashed through the flooded ground, sending up a
cataract of spray, I felt a hail of drops flung up into my
face from the hooves of the horses in front of me.

Now we turned left-handed, and the lean chestnut raced
at the ditch before us. I saw his shoes flash as he jumped,
and leaning against my bit I too raced at it with my ears
cocked. The ditch flashed below us and was gone, with a
rattle of sods kicked down by a horse that had dropped its
thin legs and by some miracle recovered.

As we turned, the long slope of the hill ran up before us,
to the farmhouse and the line of trees on the sky-line. No
longer did we know the exhilaration of galloping. Now it
became a grim business, a long struggle where muscle and

heart and lungs were worked to their utmost and every flaw was found. It was the test of stamina and training, of fitness of wind and limb.

The long climb weeded out the runners. The chestnut, his tail going up and down, his sides heaving, dropped back and back, and The Beagle took the lead, galloping steadily, with Knight of Athmore just behind him, neck and neck with Marcus and Sea Mist.

Steadily we plodded on up the hill. I could feel the ache in my quarters and loins and the muscles in my legs and neck. The wind came raw and harsh into my lungs and nostrils and the blood was hot in my head and at the back of my eyes. The sweat cooled my body with the rush through the keen thin air.

On my right galloped the sulky mare, Shannon Girl, and the black four-year-old. The hooves of the other horses faded behind us. They were out of the race.

At the end of the field two flags fluttered, marking the double ditch. A black fringe of people stood along the top of the bank on each side of the flags.

With the sun lighting up the colours and the coats of the leading horses we galloped at it. The Beagle had got his tongue over the bit now, and there was no holding him; his skimming hooves scarcely touched the top of the bank.

Side by side jumped Sea Mist and Knight of Athmore, their stirrup irons clashing. The sulky mare pulled ahead, and out of the corner of my eye I saw her ears go back. Quick as a flash she swung across to the right and ran out, carrying Shannon Girl and the black four-year-old with her.

Shannon Girl made a frantic effort to take the fence, slipped and went in on the take-off side.

The sulky mare's sideways dash almost took me with her, as I was close to the heels of Shannon Girl. But Mickey, quick as thought, swung me to the left, and we

narrowly missed disaster. I pecked on the top of the bank,
recovered, landed out over the ditch and galloped on. I felt
Mickey half out of the saddle, but somehow he worked
himself back with his hands on my neck and collected the
reins again.

The pull of the hill was beginning to tell on the leaders,
who were galloping steadily now. Even The Beagle, still in
the lead, was less headlong in his flight, and my heart was
pounding in my ribs.

Polly McCalmont was holding Marcus, who was shaking
his head. Bill Scott, leaning forward on Knight of Athmore,
was riding level with Sea Mist, who had his ears back; his
tail was swishing from side to side.

The trees in the fence to our right slid away behind us;
two of the riders spoke to each other as they galloped; a
horse moved up on my right, its nose coming to my quarter and then to my shoulder.

There were five of us now, going steadily, while the trees
and the farmhouse on top of the slope took shape and grew
larger and clearer.

I saw the white house with the sun flashing on its
windows, the shadows on the trunks of the beech-trees,
and the drifts of daffodils yellow against the short turf of
the lawn.

In front of me colours fluttered, muscular quarters
rippled and worked and bright shoes flashed to the steady
ga-ga-lump ga-ga-lump of hoof-beats.

I could hear a horse's distressed breathing, another horse
blew through his nose, and flecks of mud flew back to
us.

A flag fluttered, a fence passed, another, and another.
We crashed through a gap, and now the leaders were going
faster, the long uphill slope was passed, and we were on
level ground again. A flock of sheep in a field beside the
course wheeled and stood to watch us.

We were going along the top of the hill, where to right and left the ground sloped away in the rough squares of wide fields. Sea Mist dropped behind us, and Mickey, who had been keeping me a length behind him, let me move up. We raced down the field, and The Beagle rose at the next fence. There were bushes on the take-off side, a deep ditch flashed below us and was gone, and I jumped to one side to avoid Marcus, who skidded his own length on his side in the mud and rolled over as Polly McCalmont scrambled clear.

The tracks of the horses who had run in the first two races lay before us all the way down the hill, and half-way down the field a red flag stood by itself, and The Beagle swung round it, leaving it on his right. Mickey turned me so close to it that his boot almost touched the post.

Mad now with excitement, I felt him lean forward and give me my head. He was urging me now, and every horse was racing.

Knight of Athmore's quarters came closer to us as we crept up to him. The Beagle was coming back to us: we were gaining ground. Leaning against my bit, I came up behind them. Mud flew up in my face from their hooves, and my breath came in great gulps.

All in a bunch we jumped the fence into the plough. Down the drainage furrow Mickey held me, forcing Knight of Athmore and The Beagle to gallop on each side of it. In the plough they floundered, while my hooves were on harder going. The Beagle's rider swore under his breath.

Three heads together, three pair of hooves flashing under three outstretched noses. 'Gallop on! Gallop on! Gallop on!' they seemed to say.

On the wind a roar of voices hit us, sweeping downwards from the ridge. 'Beagle! Beagle! Athmore. Come on, Athmore!'

Heavily came the breath of the horses, thud, thud, the hooves, and the silks and white breeches were spattered with mud.

Stirrup irons clashed and rang as three abreast we shot through the gap and on to the green grass again.

Two flags; a great green bank topped by a line of Scotch fir-trees; black figures of people drawing back on each side: all came into view. The famous Cloneen double lay before us, growing higher and higher as we neared it.

I saw The Beagle cock his ears. With his roan nose in the air he raced into it. The green bank loomed above me, the poached take-off and ragged ditch below. Thud, thud, silence, grunt, thud, we were on top. Kick, thud, and we had landed on the muddy ground on the farther side and raced down the field to the last fence.

Above us the ridge, black with people, seethed and roared. I saw the white tents and the green lane through the crowd, running up to the judge-cart in a flying mist that spun before my eyes. The roaring swept us on like a mighty wave. 'Come on, The Beagle! Athmore! Athmore! Speedy!'

Every muscle strained to breaking, lungs drawing in great gulps of air, we came down the field, so close together that The Beagle's breath like steam on the air blew back into my face.

The Knight of Athmore drew away from us slowly, gaining at every stride. His shoes flashed in the late sunlight as he took the last fence.

Then he slipped, pecked on landing, and almost came down as The Beagle and I, shoulder to shoulder, landed to one side of him.

Bill Scott almost lifted him to his feet, but it was too late.

Swept forward on a flood of cheering, unconscious of anything but a giddy vision of tents and black walls of people to a green strip of course, The Beagle and I fought out the race.

Swish! Swish! Swish! went the whip on The Beagle's roan hide. Faces flashed past us, roan nose and chestnut, side by side we raced, our necks extended, each of us going our fastest and neither of us gaining on the other. I felt Mickey's heels give me the office to jump, and with a great effort I sprang forward and saw the roan nose flash back to my shoulder as we passed between the flags.

23

Goodbye, Speedy

THE crowd were all around us, and Connolly was patting Mickey on the back.

Dan was leading me along by the bridle. My sides heaved and my lungs ached. I felt the strain now as I had not done during the race. From my wet hide the steam rose in clouds on the chill air.

'Good man, Mickey!' his friends cried, and Dan slapped my dripping neck as he led me towards the weighing-in Here a space was roped off for the first, second, and third horses, and here The Beagle, Knight of Athmore, and I, steamed and got our wind again, standing in a fog of our own making.

The riders unsaddled and weighed in. Round us stood the crowd gazing curiously. 'Dan,' said a voice beside me, 'That's never the mare we sold at the auction?' 'The very same,' said Dan. Then 'How'r ye, Terry?' he exclaimed, seeing who it was. 'I heard you were in England.' 'So I am,' said Terry. 'The Captain has a big string of chasers now.'

'Ay, I heard he was training,' said Dan.

I stuck my nose out and nickered. 'Ah ha, Speedy!' said Terry, rubbing my nose. 'I always knew she was a good one,' he said.

Rubbed down and rugged up, Mickey led me along the lane. In the quiet of the spring evening everyone was going home. Strings of cars passed us, bicycles, carts, traps, and lorries, and many people on foot.

Bookies, taxis, with their boards strapped on the grids, swung down the road.

Mickey was walking on air. In his mind I expect he was

running the race again, just as I was. When he patted my neck hard, I knew that he had won it to his own satisfaction.

It was a lovely evening, and as we travelled slowly home voices came tiredly through the evening air, and far away over the beech wood I could see the rooks coming in in long straggling columns and the quick flight of pigeons dropping into the Scotch fir-trees.

Dan and Connolly met us as we walked into the yard. 'I've had an offer for the mare,' said Connolly, looking sideways. 'Will you sell her?' said Mickey. 'Yes,' said Connolly, 'it's a good offer.'

'Oh,' said Mickey flatly. Dan said nothing.

Mickey turned towards the stable door with me, and by the feel of his hand on my mane I knew that all the kick had gone out of the day for him. Perhaps he was thinking of the hunts we had had and the race, and all our days together riding and driving in the van through crooked little lanes.

He was only a kid, and for the moment all he cared for looked like being pulled about his ears.

Next morning I was tired and stiff, but when I stuck my head out over the stable door after I had finished my feed, there was something in the spring air that made me long to be out and galloping in the sunlight.

Over the fields a blackbird called. The river, steel blue, flecked by whirls and ripples, ran shining over the shallows by the cattle ford. It was a glorious day, and only Mickey looked silent and depressed.

He was kneeling down in the straw undoing one of my bandages when a long grey car came in through the yard gate, and three men and a boy stepped out of it and walked across the cobbles. It was the Captain, Terry, and John, who had grown so that I would not have known him. Dan was with them.

'Well, Mickey,' said the Captain, as the boy walked across the yard to meet them, 'we've come to look at the mare. Mr Scott was telling me about you,' he added. 'You want to be with horses, don't you?'

'I do indeed, sir,' said Mickey, wondering what was coming.

'How would you like to come over to England?' said the Captain. 'You're just the right weight, and I could do with another boy.'

Mickey's face went scarlet with excitement. All that he had wanted had suddenly and quite unexpectedly come true. In the background old Dan was grinning at him. 'We'll make a jockey out of you yet,' he said.

'You and Speedy had better come over together,' said the Captain, and so it was arranged.

The little group turned and walked away. Presently the engine roared, the car slid forward, and over the top of the wall I could see Connolly's bowler hat, Mickey's red head, and Dan's old cloth cap as they watched it going down the road until it was out of sight.